I Know You
By Heart

NAVIGATING THE DEMENTIA JOURNEY

Written by

Angie Swetland

I KNOW YOU BY HEART
Navigating the Dementia Journey

Copyright © 2020 by Angie Swetland

For permission requests, write to the publisher at:
pub@gocwpub.com

ISBN: 978-0-9889048-7-3

A **Top Kick** imprint from **Cresting Wave Publishing**, LLC
Published by Cresting Wave Publishing, LLC.

"You buy a book. We plant a tree."

Cover design: Kris and Laura Neely
Layout design: Lazar Kackarovski

Stock photography: *www.shutterstock.com*

TABLE OF **CONTENTS**

For my family with love.

With thanks to the many friends and colleagues who have shared
their stories with me over the years.

With sincere gratitude for those who have walked the Dementia
path, both those with the disease and those who have held their
hands along the way,

AND

With unmeasured appreciation for those who feel called to
serve people who struggle with brain-disabling illness. You are
motivated not by fame, or fortune, as there will be none. You
are drawn to this service for love. May God bless your lives, as
you have blessed the lives of others.

Extra thanks and hugs to W.O.S.

Thanks to Evie Waack with deep gratitude and affection.

CHAPTER 1

INTRODUCTION –
HEART AND MIND

Ella

Ella is ready.

A former church organist and choir director, she is used to looking just so. These days she might emerge from her room with her wig askew, and her lipstick crooked. Still, she always tries to look her best. Ella lives in a Memory Care Community.

Today she must go out for a doctor's appointment. I am escorting her down to wait for her ride. It is warm for March in Minnesota. Ella is wearing a boiled wool suit in emerald green with a pillbox hat and has a light woolen coat on her arm. I offer to take her coat, which she hands me with thanks. She holds her handbag prettily in both hands. No one seeing her would ever dream that this elegant lady's thoughts are blown about like sheet music in the wind. We enter the elevator with some trepidation. I know that Ella does not like elevators or closed spaces, but the stairs on her floor are secured, so this is the only exit.

The elevator is crowded. I see one resident I recognize; others in winter coats are coming to visit relatives, or here on business. It is a small space, but I count one, two, three, four, five...seven people, including Ella and me. We only have three floors to go. The door closes, and the elevator begins to descend.

Suddenly we all feel a jolt. The iron box we ride in has stopped between floors.

There is a collective intake of breath, and people express dismay. Quietly, I suggest to the man next to the emergency panel that he use the button to call for assistance. We can speak to our helpers on the outside, and they assure us that it will only be a few minutes.

Five minutes pass, then ten.

The anxiety climbs, the muttering increases. People have places they need to be. One has a dentist appointment, and another must be back at the office, a third cannot imagine not meeting her child's school bus. The other resident worries that she will miss her lunch.

I glance at Ella.

She has backed into the corner of the elevator. Her head is bowed, her shoulders hunched, her arms curled across her abdomen. She shudders. I step towards her, concerned that she is afraid, yes, but mostly worried about what she might do.

Suddenly she throws back her head, flings her arms wide, and begins to sing her favorite song, "My Wild Irish Rose," full voice. And what a lovely voice it is. I catch her eye and grin and begin to sing along.

The muttering stops.

Everyone turns to stare.

We switch from "Irish Rose" to "When Irish Eyes Are Smiling" and then to "I'll Take You Home Again Kathleen." One by one, the others join in, as we sing "Too Ra Loo Ra Loo Ra."

You see, it is St. Patrick's Day.

When the elevator doors open ten minutes later, we all exit singing.

THIRTY YEARS LATER, ON St. Patrick's Day, I like to think that somewhere in Minneapolis, someone is telling the story of that sing-along on the elevator. And the lovely lady in emerald green with a beautiful voice. They never knew she had Alzheimer's disease—all they knew was, she made them smile.

There are many articles, books, and seminars offered on the topic of dementia. Yet there never seems to be enough information to satisfy the needs of those who come face to face with this diagnosis. Whether you are a victim, a family member, an informal caregiver, or a professional caregiver, you have questions.

Some of those questions will be addressed in these pages.

First, I will share the underlying premise of this book.

Each of us is endowed at birth with gifts and a marvelously unique spirit. Whatever process or happening brings us finally to our last day, we carry that spirit with us to our final breath. Finding a path to honor that spirit, while caring for a mind and body that are being ravaged by cruel disease, is our challenge.

When symptoms of dementia begin, the people experiencing them may say to themselves or others, "I'm losing my mind!" or "I think I'm going crazy!" While it is often said half in jest, there is real fear behind it.

With some mental illness, there is hope that the disease process may be halted, and maybe what is lost can be restored through counseling and prescription therapies. There is hope that the sufferer can regain his sense of balance, perspective, and self-control.

With dementia, although medications may be helpful in many cases, the diseases described here are progressive and cannot be stopped.[1] Those with dementia do not suddenly lose their minds.

Instead, the primary functions of their brain simply seep away. Slowly, over two years or fifteen, patients lose the ability to make and keep memories, to make decisions, to control impulses.

> They do not lose their minds;
> their minds slip away.

The brain is an organ of our body, just like our lungs and our liver, and is subject to failure. People understand and accept heart and kidney failure, but brain failure seems unacceptable. This may be because we believe that our brains contain our individual humanity.

A philosopher famously said, "I think; therefore, I am."[2] Most of us accept that this is true.

Do not believe it!

We are all, and we always have been, much more than our thoughts. We are much more than our memories. We are sensory beings, gifted with feelings and depths that exceed any measure of our thinking skills.

In *Genesis 2*, we read, "And the Lord God formed man of the dust of the ground and breathed into his nostrils the breath of life; and man became a living soul." A living soul, not a body, not a mind.

You do not have to be religious to believe that there is more to man than his thoughts.

So many of the most meaningful experiences in our lives are comprised of feeling(s.) Holding your child for the first time, listening to powerful music, falling in love. In these moments, there are no words. Life's most profound experiences come in those self-forgetful, unthinking moments. Our hearts, our souls are touched.

When our cognitive gifts are depleted, and our memories are gone, we are still wholly and substantially the unique creation we have been since the day we were born. Understanding this is the key to communication and respect for those who have dementia.

The person you care for has changed,
but deep inside, they are still there.

These stories were gathered throughout a forty-year career in elder care, much of it devoted to serving those with dementia. As a family caregiver myself, I too faced many challenges.

I began my career right after college as an activity director in a nursing home. I ended my professional life as a corporate executive in a large, faith-based, not-for-profit senior care organization, operating in three states.

One of my most exceptional experiences was working with a team of nurses, social workers, and recreational therapists to put together a program to serve those with dementia. The program combined education with practice standards. This taught me the value of sharing our challenges and learning through storytelling.

In stories, you may see yourself, a loved one, a client.

Each of these vignettes is based on actual happenings, although names and details have been changed. Stories give us a chance to see ourselves in the journeys others have traveled.

The strange new road we are on has been taken before.

To love someone
is to learn their song.
And sing it to them
when they have forgotten.

~ Arne Garborg ~

CHAPTER 2

THE DISEASE—WHAT IS DEMENTIA ANYWAY?

What Is Dementia?

I should note that there are types of dementia that may be reversed—a high fever or infection generally causes these. These cases may also be referred to as delirium. Reversible dementia may be caused by medication, anesthesia, or depression. One reason for the importance of careful medical evaluation is to rule out a reversible condition.

Let's clear up some terminology.

Dementia is what we call an umbrella term—like cancer. You may have leukemia, or pancreatic cancer, or melanoma. They are all cancer. The common denominator is cells replicating abnormally and causing illness. Likewise, Lewy body disease, Alzheimer's disease, and vascular dementia are all forms of dementia.

> The common denominator is a condition that interferes with brain function, causing deterioration and a set of symptoms.[3]

Both cancer and dementia are progressive without treatment. Some cancers have effective treatments and can be cured. With the types of dementia described here, at this point, there are no known cures. When cures are found, it is likely that, just as with cancer, a treatment for one type of dementia may not cure the others.

A diagnosis of dementia generally means that the physician is not sure of the specific type of degenerative disease their patient has.

They are using the set of symptoms common to many dementias to offer a general diagnosis. There are times when having a specific diagnosis is helpful. *I am not a medical professional.* I have, however, worked with individuals suffering from the most common types of dementia. When describing them, this is as simple as it gets:

○ **Mild Cognitive Impairment (MCI)** — in MCI, there are early signs of dementia. However, the individual is still able to function independently at a reasonably high level. Although most cases of MCI do evolve into full-blown dementia with time, some do not.

○ **Alzheimer's disease (AD)** — is the most common form and is distinguished by abnormal sticky clumps called plaques and knots of cells called tangles in the brain. It progresses over time through fluid stages, from early-stage through end-stage.

○ **Vascular dementia** — is caused by vascular, or blood vessel, incidents, such as strokes or mini-strokes called transient ischemic attacks (TIAs). How fast vascular dementia progresses and the resulting symptoms depend on the frequency and location of these incidents. The disease may proceed in a stepwise fashion, with a decline following each vascular incident, followed by periods of stability in between. Or it may progress at a fairly steady pace if incidents occur frequently.

○ **Lewy body disease** — is characterized by abnormal clumps of protein, called Lewy bodies, that form inside nerve cells in the brain. These bodies are also found, in other areas of the brain, in Parkinson's disease.

○ **Frontotemporal lobar dementia** — initially attacks the frontal and temporal areas of the brain, affecting decision-making and self-control first. This is differentiated from typical Alzheimer's disease, which generally affects memory first.[4]

More detailed descriptions, including views of brain scans, can be found through the National Institutes of Health website. See Chapter 15, Helpful Websites.

There are other types of dementia, as well. Complicating matters, these diseases can co-occur in a condition known as mixed dementia.[5] Some degree of brain failure is the result of each case. As dementia progresses, the lines between the varying types start to blur as more and more of the brain is affected.

> Whatever the diagnosis, understand this:
> when you know one person with dementia,
> you know <u>one</u> person with dementia.
>
> Some symptoms are general, such as memory loss, confusion, and problems with language.[6] Other symptoms, such as mood changes, depression, and aggression, while not unusual, <u>are not universal</u>.

You may have a great-aunt or neighbor who has had dementia and think that you know what to expect. Even if your great-aunt shares the same diagnosis, the course of your disease will be just as unique as you are.

It may be slower or more swift. It may be gentler or more fierce. You will experience many of the same symptoms, but differently. The unpredictability of the course of the disease is one of its most significant challenges.

Dementia is an illness, a disease.

It is a progressive disease, meaning it is going to get worse. Some medications may slow the symptoms, but as I write this in 2020, there are no cures.

Like all diseases, it places limits on the individual struggling with it. There are things that the sufferer can no longer do well, or even do at all. This impacts the lives of those who care for that person as well. It changes the roles that the individual has held throughout their life: spouse, parent, grandparent, friend, co-worker.

There is loss.

And there is grief.

We become uneasy when symptoms first occur. As they progress, we become less and less comfortable. As the disease process moves ever forward, the sufferer loses more and more control over their memories, their actions, their bodies. Finally, they reach a point of total disease.

Much more information about dementia is available since President Reagan and other brave individuals came forward publicly with their diagnosis.

Still, much <u>misinformation</u> is also out there.

In addition to the shame and fear that often accompany the diagnosis, some misunderstand its progressive nature. A desperate son once shouted, "What do you mean she is getting worse? I put her in your memory care unit so that you could make her better!" In truth, her life was better, and his life was better. But her cognitive abilities did not improve. In fact, she continued to decline.

In addition to memory loss, other early warning signs of dementia have been identified. They include:

- changes in mood or personality
- confusion with time and place
- difficulty in planning
- difficulty with language
- misplacing things
- poor judgment
- problems with common tasks
- visual and spatial difficulties
- withdrawal from social life

Each of these will be addressed in some way in the following pages.

Memory loss is so often the first symptom people experience. What is going on here? Our memories are complicated. It is often said that we forget more than we know. How are memories made and stored? Why can even healthy people access some of them and not others?

It is a bit of a mystery, really, but some things we do know. <u>Everyone</u> forgets.

For us to make a memory, it helps to think about what is going on around us.

Have you ever lost your keys? We all have. Sometimes, when we are in a hurry and thinking about other things, we just drop them on a shelf. A memory of where we left them was never fully formed because we were not paying attention.

So much is happening in our world, all the time. Our brain has to sort through what should be stored, and what can be let go. We all simply forget at times.

As we age, there is also normal atrophy or shrinkage that occurs in the brain.[7] It may take longer to access information that is stored. The older we get, the more data files there are to sort through. Recent research indicates that we find it more challenging to filter out irrelevant information as we age.[8]

This is normal and not necessarily a sign of disease.

You're walking down the street and bump into someone you know—a classmate or work colleague you haven't seen for years. They smile and call you by name. Oh, you know them. Yet you cannot remember how. You know that face but know not the name. The more embarrassed you get, the harder it is to think.

Do not worry; this happens to all of us.

What you are worried about now, with your loved one, is different.

Our brains are complex organs. Interestingly, even those with poor recall due to dementia will remember some things. This is so confusing to family and friends, sometimes giving false hope and causing arguments about how impaired your loved one really is.

People tend to remember things that have emotional content, for instance, and information that relates to things that have always mattered to them.[9]

An older woman, who as a single mother always had to watch her pocketbook, remembers exactly how much money she made on the sale of her home. She can't recall the address or how long she lived there, just the dollars and cents.

We also form muscle memories, even when deep in dementia.

A resident living in a memory care community will often remember which chair is theirs in the dining room. After they have walked a certain number of steps, turned left, walked another series of steps, sat and risen from the same seat countless times, it becomes fixed.

It's like learning how to use a keyboard or how to bowl. At some point, your body simply catches on, and you stop thinking about each step in the process. Your muscles take over. How our minds and bodies work together is the subject of much ongoing research.

How Memory Works

The hippocampus is the area of the brain where what we do, hear, see, feel, or read enters and is transformed into a memory.[10] After a memory is formed, it is stored elsewhere in the brain. Think of it as data entry. You enter data into the processor, and then you save it to a file.

In Alzheimer's disease and other dementias, that processor is interfered with, and memories may not form in the first place. In later stages, areas of the hippocampus may be largely destroyed, and recent recall is gone.

Complicating matters is the way that the amygdala, a section of the brain involved with emotions, is involved. As information about an event in your life passes from the hippocampus to the amygdala, how you feel about it influences what you remember. Your emotions overlay the memory.

A friend spent the holidays with his younger brother. They were both in their early forties and untouched by any signs of dementia. As they discussed old times, they shared wildly different versions of the same events, even though they had both been present at the same times. Some memories were so different that both could not be true. One brother remarked, "Sometimes, I wonder if we grew up in the same house!"

Memory is not terribly reliable, which is why "eyewitness accounts" not backed up by video evidence are not all they are cracked up to be! This is as true in our living rooms as it is on the local news, or in the courtroom.

We know that the ability to form memories is affected by significant damage to the hippocampus caused by dementia. In later stages of Alzheimer's disease, in addition to other changes, long-term memories begin to erode.

Understanding the damage is occurring
in the brain will hopefully give us more patience
as we ponder where this path is headed.

Some people say that Alzheimer's disease has three stages, some say five, others say seven.[11] Yet the condition is fluid, and an individual may seem to be in stage three one day, and stage two the next.

For that reason, this book talks about only three: beginning, middle, and end. The words *dementia* and *Alzheimer's disease* are used interchangeably at times, simply because AD is so much more common than other types. Some readers are professional caregivers, and some are dementia patients. Many are family caregivers. In this book, for the sake of consistency, those with the disease are generally referred to as "your loved one" or "the patient."

She walks into an empty room
"I'm here," she calls
Over there, a mirror
She gazes into it
"Not me," she thinks
Too old, too…
A stranger
She looks again, sees,
Sighs.
"I slipped my mind"

CHAPTER 3

IT BEGINS – EARLY STAGE

Memory Loss — June

It has been five years since June moved in as one of the first tenants in a new senior citizen community. She and the other early birds, known as the pioneers, have formed a tight-knit group of friends.

At eighty-two, she is always moving, a tiny, spry dynamo topped with a head of pure white curls. A widow for twenty years, she is strong, independent and proud of her ability to manage on her own.

She is starting to be a little forgetful, so she relies on a daily calendar to keep her on track. She still drives, offering rides to others when they need one. June is the backbone of the Activity Committee. Today at seven o'clock is the annual Valentine's Day celebration. At one o'clock, committee members gather in the party room to decorate and finalize details about entertainment and refreshments.

I am at my desk in the manager's office, trusting the activity director and the committee to do their usual excellent job. At two o'clock, there is a knock at my door. Sally, June's best friend, pops her head in, "Do you know where June is? I stopped by her apartment to remind her about the meeting, but she isn't there."

I shake my head.

It is unlike her to miss a commitment, but she is only an hour late. A half-hour later, I go to join in the preparations.

Still no June.

Afterward, I head back to my office and circle my desk to sit. Just then, I hear a timid knock at the door. This is followed by the welcome sight of June's curly-topped head peeping around the door.

Sheepishly, June enters and sits. "June, we missed you!" I say.

She begins to tremble, and tears form in the corners of her eyes. I walk over to sit beside her. "I'm so sorry," she begins as she stares down at her hands, limp in her lap. "I went out to pick up some groceries at the store just down the hill. I left at eleven, so I knew that I had plenty of time to get back and have some lunch before the meeting. When I left the store, I could not find my car! I think I was remembering my old blue Chevy, but my new car—the one I got when I moved here—is white. After I got in, as I left the parking lot, I couldn't remember which way to turn. I've been driving around for over two hours!"

The tears begin to flow, followed by sobs. I hug her and tell her it will be OK, but my heart sinks. She is shaken by her experience and ashamed of her failure. She is afraid for the future. I hold her hand and can't help but tear up too.

Dementia is progressive. This is an independent living community with few services available. I fear that we are going to lose June. On a deeper level, and infinitely sad, she is afraid that she will lose herself.

How does it start?

Mom's doctor's appointments forgotten, her favorite necklace misplaced, utility bills unpaid. Perhaps your typically witty, gentle, and thoughtful husband begins making dubious investments and rude, unkind remarks.

Let's begin with mom's forgetfulness.

> A lack of recall is one of the earliest and most familiar symptoms of Alzheimer's disease, the most prevalent form of dementia.[12]

Actually, mom remembers many things quite well.

What you notice is an inability to recall most,
but not all, recent events or current deadlines.

This is so confusing because one day, you will be terribly concerned, and the next, you are reassured that "she is fine." Making lists helps for a while until she can't remember to look at the list.

Still, we are left with the question—what now? What do we do when June has lost her way on a ten-minute drive that she has made at least weekly for five years? Or when mom is not taking her medication on time, or maybe not at all.

Or, fill in the blank.

In June's case, the first step was to stop driving. There was no need to confront her and ask her to stop driving. She was too afraid to get behind the wheel again. Family and friends stepped in to assist with transportation, and she began to ride the community van.

Within months, home care services were arranged to set up medications.

Next, housekeeping and laundry services were added.

Then, bathing assistance was given.

Eventually, a move to assisted living was necessary.

Later, financial and medical considerations combined to require nursing home placement.

The next chapter offers resources and support that *you* may want to access.

Confusion and Difficulty with Familiar Tasks — Frances

Frances lived at the end of the wing in the lovely senior apartment building I managed. She and Mabel, her neighbor across the hall, both had large units positioned directly above the entrance to the underground parking garage. Frances was happily independent and pleased with her lovely home.

Frances and Mabel only had one complaint. The garage door would open and close at night, disturbing Mabel's sleep and Frances's weeknight date with "The Tonight Show."

Repeated checks of the garage door opener revealed no problems. Oh, and Frances was having trouble with her TV. There was nothing wrong with her connection to the rooftop antenna.

Now, this was back in the days when TV repairmen had local shops and even came to your home to fix your set. The repairman had been to look at Frances's TV and found nothing wrong. Her TV seemed to work fine whenever someone else was there.

One afternoon, Frances stepped into the office, agitated and distressed. She had been out running errands. As she approached the apartment building and reached for the garage remote, she could not find it. She parked outside and searched her car. No remote. She dumped her purse on my desk. No remote. Together, we examined both her car and her apartment.

Still no remote.

Frances drove an old car, and never saw much sense in locking it. We had to assume the remote control had been stolen. Well, this was a pretty big deal for us. There were eighty garage stalls, and eighty openers that needed to be reprogrammed, as well as the garage door itself. It was a late night for the staff.

The next day, the TV repairman was back in our building to see another tenant. He stopped in the office. "I knocked at Frances's door, but she seems to be out. Can I leave something for her?"

"Of course," I replied. He had a manila envelope in his hand.

"She came in when we were busy yesterday and dropped off this envelope, saying she needed her TV remote control repaired," he began, "but this isn't a TV remote."

He opened the envelope and tipped a garage door opener into my hand.

Frances had been pointing her garage door opener at the TV, trying to turn the sound down during commercials. Of course, the volume did not change. The garage door responded, though, by opening and closing, right up until the time that "The Tonight Show" signed off. Mystery solved!

Frances's story is a reminder that sometimes confusion, a problem with word-finding, or an inability to use familiar objects is the first sign of dementia. Her recall of recent events had not been a concern.

Her symptoms continued to increase, and Alzheimer's disease was the eventual diagnosis.

Poor Judgment — George

During World War II, George served his country, as so many of his generation did. Because he had a great mind for math and puzzles, he was assigned to the code-breaking unit.

George moved into a memory care community after his lack of self-care and poor decision-making placed him at serious risk. To enter or exit the memory care community, you had to enter a four-digit code into a keypad near the door. The code was changed periodically, but it was usually based on something staff could easily remember—the year that the building was built, the last four digits of the main phone number, the building address.

George's recall of the recent past and his reasoning abilities were intact. He figured out the code three times and got away. Fortunately, he was quickly found and returned each time. The community had to switch to using random codes and changing them frequently to outfox George!

> Some forms of dementia do not affect the memory or cause confusion initially but instead affect what is known as executive function.

Decision-making may be impaired first, and even the ability to protect oneself may be lessened. Impulse control may be diminished. Ordinary filters, which keep us from saying or doing whatever pops into our minds, are gone.[13]

These forms of dementia attack the brain's frontal lobe first, command central for our behavior. Mental illness may be suspected or even a mid-life crisis. The brain is undergoing a destructive change, a form of dementia that brings unique challenges.

This may be referred to as frontotemporal lobar dementia (FTD).[14]

People with this diagnosis may take extraordinary risks, such as stepping directly in front of a moving vehicle, without regard to safety. Yet they never forget an appointment, a birthday, or an anniversary.

George retained his cleverness, his ability to problem-solve. He did not make appropriate decisions about virtually any aspect of his life.

Those with FTD are especially challenged, as are those who live with them. The vital task for caregivers is finding a way to protect the individual as well as themselves. The person with the disease may not agree that they have any issues. Risks they take may affect the safety of those who live with them. They may be uncharacteristically unkind and uncaring, even abusive. Others who spent little time with them do not realize the depth of the problem.

It is essential if you suspect FTD,
to seek medical advice. And find yourself
a reliable support system.

Eventually, as FTD progresses, other areas of the brain will be affected. Memory loss and confusion will often occur.[15] The lines between FTD and Alzheimer's disease may blur.

Hallucinations — Dorothy

Dorothy was living happily in her lovely little apartment home. She did her shopping, lunched with friends, and enjoyed going out to play bingo. She liked to be home by 5:30, so she could watch the news and then her favorite: "Wheel of Fortune!"

One day, the manager stopped by to drop off some paperwork regarding her lease. He happened to arrive just as she sat down for dinner at her little table for four. She invited him to sit and join her for a cup of coffee. Then she stepped away to get the pot.

He noticed she had two place settings out and pulled out a chair. "No!" she exclaimed as she returned with a third cup. "Not that chair, can't you see that Tom is already sitting there?"

Puzzled, the manager asked, "Tom, who?" "Why Tom Brokaw, of course. He always joins me for dinner." At that moment, the voice of Tom Brokaw broke in, introducing breaking news.

Another type of dementia that has unique features is Lewy body dementia (LBD). It is not caused by damage due to the plaques and tangles of Alzheimer's disease or the blood vessel damage of vascular dementia. It is caused instead by tiny bodies in the brain called Lewy bodies. These Lewy bodies are identical to the ones found in the brains of those with Parkinson's disease; the difference lies in the brain in which they are found.[16]

An unusual symptom of LBD, which occurs in up to 80% of all cases, is the presence of hallucinations.[17]

Interestingly, most hallucinations that accompany LBD are of people and animals.[18]

Curiously, there are several tales of women who see rabbits — rabbits in boxes, rabbits behind the curtains, rabbits under the bed. Some hallucinations accompanying Lewy body disease may not trouble the individual with this type of dementia, although they are more than a little disconcerting to everyone else. In other cases, the hallucinations may be quite frightening.

In any case, the presence of these visions should be shared with medical professionals, and a diagnosis should be sought, preferably by a doctor who is familiar with dementia.

The presence of hallucinations in the general population may lead to a prescription for anti-psychotic medications. However, these drugs may exacerbate symptoms of Lewy body disease.[19] There are resources and information specific to LBD on the websites of the Alzheimer's Association and the National Institutes of Health (See chapter 15.) There may be LBD-specific support groups in your area as well.

Although Dorothy's hallucinations indicated a need for further evaluation, they caused her no concern.

Elizabeth, however, was a different matter.

Changes in Mood and Perception, Misplacing Things — Elizabeth

Elizabeth is tiny and shy. She reminds me of a little bird, a wren, or a sparrow.

She tries not to call attention to herself, but my eyes are drawn to her as she flits from kitchen to bedroom. She has selected the smallest apartment in the brand-new over-55-only apartment complex.

Back in the office, she assures me that she loves living independently and needs no services. She is "just fine," she says. I remind her that while we do offer one optional meal a day in our restaurant, we do not provide medical care. She smiles gently, eyes lowered to the paper in front of her, and signs the lease.

As the weeks pass, she makes few friends, but smiles and flaps her hand in greeting as she picks up her mail. She pays her rent promptly, coming to the office to personally hand me the check.

Otherwise, she keeps to herself.

The other residents, who frequently gather for potluck dinners, cards, and outings, have made overtures and been rebuffed. Offended to their Midwestern cores, they have decided she is an "odd duck." Feeling protective, I try to stifle these comments when I hear them.

But several weeks into her stay, Elizabeth begins to show signs that concern me.

It's Monday, and I arrive bearing my cup from Caribou Coffee. While fumbling with my keys, I hear a tiny panicked voice from the chair just opposite the office door. "There you are! Where have you been?"

It is Elizabeth.

She follows me in and proceeds to tell me that we must change the lock to her apartment door because she is sure that someone has been in her apartment and stolen things. We talk, and I understand that what has been taken is an unlikely trio of items: a hairbrush, the dress she wore to her daughter's wedding fifteen years ago, a brand-new unopened box of Tide.

I accompany her to her apartment.

We find the hairbrush, hidden in the bottom of a drawer. The Tide is located in the communal laundry room, where she also left her laundry basket. And the dress? Maybe it didn't make the move with her.

She cannot let it go; she is afraid. In the end, we change her lock.

There are voices and noises in the night. She hears people talking about her. Well, to be fair, this is a place where everybody talks about everybody. Now she hears knocks on the door in the middle of the night. People in the apartment above her are making noise, just to disturb her and keep her from sleeping.

We examine each complaint but find nothing to substantiate her worries.

As weeks go by, the frequency of complaints increases and her anxiety multiplies.

I am concerned.

Is Elizabeth experiencing signs of a type of dementia, or is this mental illness? She should see a geriatric psychiatrist or neurologist to find out what is going on. I contact the adult children she has named as designated representatives, but they are busy and seem unconcerned. Maybe they are tired of coping with the changes in their mother.

In any case, Elizabeth is paying her rent, not bothering other residents, and generally a good tenant. These are senior apartments, not assisted living, and her health issues are a private matter.

We carry on.

Problems are always worse on Mondays or whenever I have been away for a few days. For a time, it seems that I am the only one she trusts.

Until one day, I look up to see a police officer standing at the door to my office. He's someone I haven't met. "Are you Angie Swetland?" he asks, rather sternly.

I nod.

"We've had a complaint about you, from Elizabeth B. in apartment 216. She tells us that you will not allow her to go out, that you are in effect holding her hostage. You cannot keep her here, you know, ma'am. She has a right to leave."

I try smiling at him, but he frowns. He is deadly serious!

I really cannot believe this. I reply, "Oh, Officer, please go up and see her. She has a perfect right to leave. She is quite fearful, though, so you'll want to be extra gentle!"

He raises his eyebrows, frowns again, and heads for the elevator.

Twenty minutes later, I hear an ambulance arriving. The somewhat sheepish policeman stops in my office. He says, "The apartment door was open when I went in, and I found her standing on the toilet seat in the bathroom, talking to voices she swears are coming from the ceiling vent. She seems to feel there is a conspiracy against her. The EMTs are taking her into the hospital on a seventy-two-hour psychiatric hold."

The eventual diagnosis was Lewy body disease.

Over time, this police officer had occasion to visit many times and became a good friend of staff and residents.

Elizabeth did not return.

Her family gave notice, letting us know that she moved into a specialized memory care community following her hospital stay. I was sorry to see her go, but I sincerely hope she found both loving care and a place to live where she felt both free and safe.

Elizabeth experienced not just hallucinations; she was also fearful and suspicious.

These feelings may be present not only in Lewy body disease but also in other types of dementia.

Frustrated when unable to find possessions they have misplaced, angry at their confusion, irritated by their own ability to remember, patients may lash out at others.

It is so hard to admit that our own mind is failing us. It is much easier to place the blame elsewhere.

Young Onset Dementia

Although most people experiencing symptoms of dementia are in their later years, there are cases diagnosed at a younger age. "Young onset" or

"Early onset" is generally defined as dementia beginning before the age of sixty-five.[20]

I know individuals who began
their dementia journey while still in their
late forties and early fifties.

These diseases are always a challenge for families. For younger people, they are particularly tragic. A daughter, still in high school, watching her mother lose her memories. A wife, watching her husband lose his ability to coach the team, or even to go to work. A spouse responsible for raising children, taking care of a dependent spouse, and holding a full-time job, while quite possibly also being responsible for an aging parent.

Those who receive this diagnosis themselves are doubly devastated. How dreadful to know that those who need you daily will someday no longer be able to rely on you. *Still Alice*, a novel by Lisa Genova, explores young onset thoughtfully and compassionately.

The genetic component of dementia looms large in some of these cases. Research continues to determine the inheritability of various dementias. We do know that there are clearly types of young onset that have a genetic component and can be inherited.[21]

Families of young onset victims may want to
consider having genetic testing done.

Seek medical, social services, and legal support and advice. Accept the help of family, friends, your faith community, and other community agencies. This road is much too hard to walk alone.

Events like those described in this chapter are the moments when we realize that there is more going on than simple forgetting. The moment we feared has come.

The moment we say, "Something has to be done."

CHAPTER 4

RESOURCES AND SUPPORT PART 1 – WHAT NOW?

Step By Step

The field of eldercare offers several services. It can be complicated, and you need to be a good shopper and an even better advocate for yourself and your loved one.

At this point, you are reasonably sure you are dealing with dementia.

What do you do now?

You may be looking for different levels of assistance as the disease progresses. This chapter considers some resources you may want to use while your loved one is still able to live at home. By the time you read this book, the landscape will no doubt have changed, and hopefully, even more resources will be available.

Perhaps you do not yet have a diagnosis of dementia; you just recognize the symptoms.

When you turn sixty-five, your doctor is likely to administer a brief assessment of your mental status during your annual physical. It might include remembering a string of unrelated words and drawing a clock. If you do poorly, a note will be made in your chart, and you might be referred for further testing.

While this brief test measures a couple of areas of thinking (cognition), it does not capture all of the domains that can be measured. It may point out a problem that needs further examination. It may also miss certain types of dementia that do not initially affect memory.

Please be sure to share any causes for concern with your primary physician.

When seeking a diagnosis, it is essential to rule out other causes of forgetfulness and confusion, such as medications, depression, and infection. Further exams may be necessary.

Cognitive assessments (assessments of thinking skills) may be given at a memory care clinic, in a neurologist's office, or by a geriatric psychologist or geriatric psychiatrist. Your primary physician should be able to help you with a referral.

Resources for Support and Education

The Alzheimer's Association offers telephone support, support groups, education, and downloadable information on a variety of related topics. They also raise funds for critical research that may someday bring a cure. In addition to the national organization, there are local chapters across the country and the globe.

The National Institutes of Health (NIH) operates the Alzheimer's Disease Education and Referral Center (ADEARS), which provides support and information. There are downloadable articles and free booklets and publications available through their website.

Other sources of information include county social services, your physician's office, your area agency on aging, local service organizations, and your faith community.

Care and Services for Those Living at Home

If you are looking for practical help with meals, chores, and housekeeping or need in-home health care services, there are local agencies that may help.

Some services may be free, some come at a cost, and some may be available on a sliding fee scale. Your state or county Department of Health and Human Services or area agency on aging can be of valuable assistance, particularly when financial resources are limited. In Minnesota, where I live, the Senior Linkage Line is a statewide telephone service that provides guidance and referrals for anyone needing information regarding elder care.

Check to see if such a resource is available in your area.

Many people think immediately of residential options such as assisted living, memory care assisted living, and nursing homes. But there are several services available before you are ready to make such a move. A few of the possible services you may choose include:

- ○ Support groups for caregivers and dementia patients (often held separately)
- ○ Emergency pendants
- ○ Medical Alert ID bracelets
- ○ Chore services (lawn mowing, snow shoveling, etc.)
- ○ Homemaking services (housekeeping, laundry)
- ○ Meal services (delivered meals or congregate dining)
- ○ Transportation services (for doctor's appointments, errands, etc.)
- ○ Home health services (for assistance with medications, bathing, etc. This could be every other week, or it could be twenty-four hours a day depending on need)
- ○ Adult day center (providing supervised activities at a center, typically open during the standard workweek)
- ○ Respite care
  - **In-home**—volunteers or home care staff who will stay with your loved one for a few hours while you shop or run errands
  - **Residential**—typically an assisted living or nursing home providing temporary accommodations for several days while you attend an out-of-town wedding, see to your own medical needs, or for a period of recuperation.
- ○ Individuals or agencies offer geriatric case management. A case manager, often a licensed social worker, can arrange for and

manage services, as well as assist with finances and medical appointments

You are likely to have a friend, relative, or neighbor who relies on one or more of these services.

> It is always wise, when possible,
> to get a referral from someone you know and trust,
> especially for services that are provided in-home.

Some of these services may come through a block nurse program, a parish nurse, a neighborhood organization, county social services, or a home care business.

Neighbors and friends may be enlisted to check up on your loved one if you live far away or are unavailable for any reason. Faith communities may have friendly visitor, Befriender, or Stephen's Minister programs, which can provide companionship and skilled listeners. Check with your church, synagogue, or mosque. Organizations such as Jewish Family Services, Lutheran Social Services, or Catholic Charities are also good sources of support or referral.

Leona (Mom)

My mom seldom left her home. She went out to dinner weekly with a friend. My husband or I took her to all of her necessary appointments. We occasionally brought over groceries.

He and I were still working full-time, so days would go by without our seeing her. She was content spending much of her time alone. She had her dog, Shadow, well-named as he never left her side, and for the most part, that was enough company for her. She let Shadow out on a chain, as she was no longer able to take him for walks.

She had a car but only drove two miles to the grocery store and back. This restriction was self-imposed, because she once got lost, and it scared her. We got her an emergency pendant and set her up with "Meals on Wheels." Some programs send frozen meals once a week, but my mom got them delivered to her door Monday through Friday. They rang the doorbell, and she went to the door to pick them up. If she was going to be away, we notified "Meals on Wheels," and they skipped that day. If she was supposed to be home but did not answer the door, they called her. Their policy was to call me when she didn't answer her phone or the doorbell. It gave me great peace of mind knowing that she had nutritious meals and saw someone face-to-face five days a week.

There were seldom issues.

Except for the time — It was Thursday, about noon. I was out of town for the annual meeting of Leading Age, an association representing senior care providers. We met "Up North" as we say in Minnesota, on a lovely lake about three hours north of home. I was grabbing a cup of coffee before a session when my phone rang.

I saw the caller ID identifying "Meals on Wheels." The kind but concerned woman on the phone let me know that Mom did not respond to her door or the phone. Mom had greeted them at the door as usual on Wednesday, but today she did not answer.

I said, "Thank you," and hung up. I dialed Mom's landline. No answer.

Thinking she might have gone to get groceries, I waited a half an hour and called again. No answer.

We had given Mom a cell phone, but she did not use it. I called it anyway. Still no answer.

Of course, I feared that she had fallen. It would not have been the first time.

Finally, I called my husband, Doug, and asked him to drive the forty-five minutes to her home and check on her. We had the key to her front door. Meanwhile, I kept on calling.

Doug arrived, only to discover that not only had she locked her front door, but she had also locked her screen door—to which we had no key. He got some tools from his Jeep and started to remove the screen so that he could reach in and unlatch the screen door.

He was almost in when a neighbor cautiously approached and asked him what he was doing. He explained. She was a little skeptical and said that she thought she should call the police. "That's probably a good idea," he replied.

So, she did.

A police officer arrived, listened to his story, saw that he had a key to the front door, and entered the house with him. They walked through the house and the garage and noted that the car was there, but the dog was gone. They locked up, and the policeman left.

We reasoned that she must have gone on a planned outing since Shadow was gone too. I assumed that she would be back soon. I contacted "Meals on Wheels" to thank them and asked that they deliver a meal on Friday as usual.

I was still anxious. I was not able to reach her until late that evening.

She explained that her friend had picked her up Wednesday afternoon after lunch. They had gone to the casino for an overnight gambling excursion!

We still laugh about that story.

It is not every day that someone calls the police on you! But the whole experience was reassuring. We knew that she was forgetful, and we weren't surprised that she forgot to let us know about her outing. The good news was that the measures we put in place worked the way they were supposed to. The "Meals on Wheels" staff followed their procedures and called me. My husband was available to check on her, armed with the key to her door. A watchful neighbor stepped in. The police were helpful and ready to act if she did not return soon.

In-Home Respite

I want to mention respite particularly, because it has been especially useful in my family, and because it is not widely known. Living with someone with dementia can be so confining.

> Many people living with dementia
> reach a point where outings are confusing and upsetting.

Still, the caregiver needs to get out to run errands, attend worship services, or just get a breath of fresh air. Having someone come and stay with your loved one for a few hours once or twice a week is so beneficial.

Ask a friend, neighbor, or family member if they are willing to help.

Some local service organizations may offer
this service for free or on a sliding scale.
If free respite care is not available in your area,
a home care agency can provide this service at a cost.

Residential Respite

Residential respite care is offered by some (but not all) assisted living, nursing home, and residential hospice centers. Three members of our family have taken advantage of this program for recuperative periods.

Offering a furnished room, meals,
housekeeping, laundry, and arranged
for health care services, it is a good short-term choice when
the individual temporarily has no caregiver able to provide
twenty-four-hour attention.

It may also be an option when the home environment is not
conducive to recuperation following a hospital stay when a
skilled nursing stay in a rehabilitation center is not required or
approved by Medicare.

If the individual qualifies for in-home Medicare-covered therapy services, they can be provided in residential respite care, just as they are in one's own home. However, the cost of room, board, and daily assistance is typically paid for privately.

Residential respite is usually offered on a time-limited basis.

Providers who offer respite stays will differ in their requirements, but a stay of no less than five days and no more than one month is standard.

Hospital discharge and social services staff
may not be well acquainted with residential respite care, as
their focus is on returning the individual home.
You may have to call assisted living centers directly to find
out about openings.

Sadly, this service is not available in all areas.

Residential respite care is also a good choice when your loved one is healthy and at home, but the primary caregiver is hospitalized or wishes to attend an out-of-town wedding. Or just needs a break.

Some residential hospice homes offer this service for individuals who are receiving hospice care. Their hospice benefit under Medicare may cover this. It provides a much-needed break so that primary caregivers can see to their own health care needs, or even take a brief vacation.

Making a move to assisted living or a nursing home is addressed in a later chapter.

However, a word to the wise is timely.

Perhaps you know someone who says, "I promised my mom that I would never put her in a nursing home."

If you have never made this promise, please do not.

You cannot know what circumstances may arise to limit your ability to care for a loved one at home. A time may arrive when you are at your wits' end, and your health becomes compromised. If you have not seen an assisted living community or been in a nursing home in the last ten years, I invite you to visit.

Most have changed so much for the better.

If you *have* made such a promise, please consider both your loved one's safety and your physical, mental, and emotional well-being. Believe this: It is OK to break a promise when keeping the promise will break you.

CHAPTER 5

IT'S NOT UNUSUAL – **MIDDLE STAGE**

Nothing Changes But Change

W. Edward Deming is quoted as saying, "Two basic rules of life are:

- ○ Change is inevitable, and
- ○ Everybody resists change.[22]

Your loved one is going through changes that you will both resist. He or she may behave in ways that are surprising and often distressing. They will act in ways that are out of character for them, and outside of societal norms.

In the context of the dementia process, however, they are not unusual.

Changes in Hygiene — Leona (Mom)

Mom was always proud of her appearance—her hair, her skin, her clothes. She was tall and slender. When she was younger, people said that she should have been a model. Her hair was blond as a child but began to darken as she got older, so off to the salon she went.

When we were growing up, she regularly went to the salon, where her hair was colored, permanent waved, and teased into a sleek helmet. She wore a hairnet to bed and a plastic rain hat when it rained or snowed. When we wanted a hug, we had to approach cautiously, to avoid mussing up her hair. In the mornings, she did not brush it or comb it but used a pick to lift it into place.

She worked the day shift as a nurse, which meant that she left the house before seven each day. I never had to set the alarm for school. The scent of hairspray wafting down the hall woke me.

She was committed to her beauty routine, and though the family sometimes struggled to pay the electric bill, Mom never missed a hair appointment. It was disconcerting when in her eighties, she began to lose interest in her appearance.

As a registered nurse, she was aware of proper bodily care.

But she stopped bathing regularly, instead washing occasionally with a cloth at the sink. To be sure that she smelled OK, she sprayed on perfume. She used so much that her clothing, car, and home reeked of it.

She gave up coloring her hair.

Then she stopped getting perms and even cuts.

Though I offered to make appointments and take her, she would not go.

One Sunday, we dropped by her place to take her out. She greeted us as we walked in, sitting on her couch with her hair pulled back, Alice in Wonderland style, tied with a big yellow ribbon. On closer inspection, we realized that the "ribbon" was the plastic sleeve from her Sunday newspaper, twisted and tied in a bow.

I asked her if she would like some cute headbands.

She agreed and happily wore her hair loosely combed and pulled back with inexpensive elastic bands.

A COMMON CONCERN AMONG FAMILY members is the lack of attention to personal hygiene. Left on their own, some will fail to get dressed for days on end. Women who wouldn't dream of going out to check the mail without lipstick will go unwashed, with hair matted and tangled. Proudly clean-shaven men will grow a spotty, scruffy beard.

What is behind this?

In some cases, depression may be a factor. Depression and dementia commonly occur together.[23] If there is nowhere to go, why get ready?

Often, the sufferer is unclear about the time of day and doesn't realize that it is time to get dressed. In some cases, day/night inversion may occur.[24] In this strange phenomenon, the person with dementia may be up all night and sleep all day.

> If your loved one is refusing to get dressed,
> you might check on the fit of the clothing in their closet.
> It may be that she has lost or gained weight.

> Be sure to check the underclothes.
> Maybe you've made sure to provide new slacks
> and tops as mom gained weight, but her underwear
> is still two sizes too small.
>
> She resists getting dressed
> *because she is miserable when she does!*
> Comfortable clothing and footwear are <u>a priority.</u>

People may also drape themselves with multiple layers of clothing in odd combinations. Or they may decide to disrobe unashamedly. This is not typically sexual in any way; they are just trying to be comfortable. Perhaps their bodies do not feel temperature the same way as we do. Maybe they feel encumbered. Experiment with clothing that is wonderfully comfortable or difficult to remove.

> Giving patients something to manipulate
> with their hands, like a stress ball or non-toxic clay,
> can help distract those who tug at their clothing.

People may resist showering or bathing because of fear of falling. The white shower stall or tub on the white floor is hard to distinguish. Another concern may be the water itself. Water is clear and may not be visible, so stepping into a running shower or full bath may be very startling.

Giving verbal cues such as "the water is running"
or "the tub is full, watch your step" may help.
Combine oral with tactile cues—"Is this water the right
temperature?"—as you splash a few drops on her arm.

Do remember that older skin cannot tolerate very hot water,
and think about setting the thermostat on the water heater
down. Recognize that for most older adults,
<u>showering every day is not necessary</u>.

Many of us may find that shocking, but skin does
become thin and dry as we age. Too frequent bathing further
dries the skin.

Some older people have always used a bathtub and are not used to showers. They might dislike the feeling of water falling on their heads. Maybe using a hand-held wand would be more successful.

One patient would forget all about being showered if her caregiver sang to her. She would sing and hum along, and all was well.

We are each unique, so you need to be creative.

Use bath chairs, soft towels, soft music. Growing up, many elders only took one bath a week, usually after a hard day of work or play. Often this was Saturday evening, so they would be ready to wear their Sunday best for church. Or maybe it was Sunday evening, to be fresh for the new school week.

Try giving the reluctant bather a reason
to get clean, one that resonates with their past.

Changes in Appetite — Millie

People with dementia may experience changes in their appetite.[25] Left to themselves, they may eat all the time, or not at all. They may want to eat only one food and refuse all else. Their life-long sweet tooth or craving for salty, savory foods may be gone.

Millie loved her breakfast.

She was hungry all morning long. She never gained or lost weight. Physically fit and restless, she roamed the halls all day, barely sitting down for lunch or dinner, no matter how much we encouraged her. Early each day, she wolfed down eggs, pancakes, and fruit. She asked for the same breakfast each day.

The dining room was always open, and the staff was used to serving Millie throughout the morning. She would finish a meal, wander away, and then return for more.

In December, we hired an excellent new maintenance man, Marv. He had never worked with seniors, so he was scheduled for the required dementia care training in January. He enjoyed visiting with the residents as he went about his work.

One morning we closed down the dining room after breakfast to set up for a special holiday luncheon. Employees were putting up decorations when suddenly Marv burst through the door. He was upset. "Millie is crying; she says she's had nothing at all to eat and is so hungry! Can't we get her some food?" The food service director just smiled and replied, "Of course, bring her in. But Marv, this will be her third breakfast this morning."

Millie's diet included fruit, carbohydrates, and protein. The cooks prepared omelets with sweet pepper and mushroom, used a vegetable garnish, and served her meals with a large glass of tomato/vegetable juice.

She downed it all with relish.

Despite her limited tastes, when combined with a daily multi-vitamin, her diet was probably better than that of many Americans. However, there are those whose choices are less nutritious.

In another situation, a daughter was quite concerned when her mother would only eat breakfast cereal, three meals a day, and for a snack. Of course, she was worried that her mother's overall health would suffer. Yet she could not convince her mother to eat anything else, and force-feeding was certainly not an option. So she chose the most nutritious cereals possible, with nuts for protein. She served it with fruit on top and plenty of milk. It was served with orange or vegetable juice, and a good multi-vitamin.

If faced with this dilemma, remember that
this phase may pass, so continue to offer other foods.
One day, your loved one may surprise you, and decide that
a hamburger or salad looks appealing.

Other food-related issues are not uncommon.

My mom had always been a stickler for table manners, setting the table with napkins, glasses, and silver all in their proper places. As early-stage dementia set in, she began to put her food on paper towels and to eat with her fingers, licking her fingers between each bite.

She frequently spilled on her clothing—all without seeming to notice, and she still loved to go out for meals.

I worried that her lack of manners would draw unwanted attention, so I devised a strategy. Her favorite dinner was crab legs, so when we went out, I took her to Red Lobster, ordered the "all you can eat" crab legs, and asked for a lobster bib. At another restaurant, her favorite was the chicken salad sandwich. Since both of these menu items are mostly finger food, her manners didn't matter. This normally fastidious woman was no longer interested in the polite conventions that had meant so much to her.

I had to make adjustments to my attitude
and realize that they weren't so important after all.

There may be another factor at work here. As dementia progresses, communication between the brain and the body is affected.

In a condition called apraxia, the ability to
carry out a familiar movement is lost. Fine motor skills
are lost, and the use of utensils becomes difficult.

First to go are actions that require the use of two implements, such as cutting meat with a knife and fork.

Later, even using a spoon is more than some can manage. At this point, finger foods are a good option. Spoon-feeding is a last resort, as it reduces the dignity of the patient and increases the workload of the caregiver.

Still later, apraxia affects large motor movements. Your loved one may shuffle her feet. Even while still physically capable of bending, she may lose the ability to sit down in a chair and rise again without assistance.

> This is the time to do an environmental scan. Examine your loved one's living environment and remove any items, such as scatter rugs, that may cause a fall.

Mom was an organized, good cook, and an excellent baker. As time went on, she began to make mistakes in the kitchen.

We sat down to Thanksgiving dinner to find that the turkey was underdone. The potatoes for her famous mashed potatoes, peeled and in the pot, had not been put on to boil. We just turned the burner on under the potatoes and stuck the turkey back in the oven for another hour. At Christmas, she baked a batch of her famous raisin sugar cookies using a cup of salt instead of a cup of sugar.

We were always asking if she was ready to move to a senior apartment. But she had been a fiercely independent single working woman for over twenty years. It took years of scraping and saving to able to buy her own home. Any talk of moving was quickly shut down.

Luckily, until the last two weeks of her life, she was able to remain living alone. She had the support of frequent visits and phone calls, "Meals on Wheels" delivered five days a week and an emergency pendant. We used residential respite care when she needed extra attention following a hospital stay. When she was ill, we added home health visits until she was back on her feet. Her final two weeks were spent in a comfortable room in an excellent nursing home.

We were so lucky.

Changes in Eyesight and Perception — Rita

Rita got around the assisted living building just fine. She came from a large family, and the homey atmosphere, with lots of people around, suited her perfectly. That is until new carpeting was installed. A pale green carpet with a simple pattern covered the center of the dining room. Surrounding this was a wide border of deep forest green. Everyone agreed that it was just lovely.

Except for Rita.

To her eyes, the wide dark border was a deep hole. The dining tables were all floating in the middle of a moat. She refused to go in.

Our eventual solution was to place her in a wheelchair, with her back to the border, and back her into and out of the dining room. Once she was seated at her place at the table, she was fine.

Changes in vision that occur with dementia may not be obvious. The individual may still be able to read an eye chart and pass a vision test.

Yet other changes, such as motion blindness, lack of depth perception, muddied colors, and changes in peripheral vision, are common as the disease progresses.[26]

This means that the individual may be startled if someone comes at them directly from the left or right.

In fact, it is always best to approach someone from the front at a slight angle. Standing directly in front of someone feels confrontational to many.

As the disease progresses, it can be difficult to distinguish an object from the field behind it. A slice of turkey and mashed potatoes on a white or off-white plate can disappear. Using plates in colors that food seldom comes in may help. There are few blue foods, for instance.

A white toilet against a light beige wall sitting on a white tile floor may not be seen.

There have been cases when "incontinence" issues have *disappeared* with the application of brightly colored paint and the use of a black toilet seat!

Speaking of urination, I do not recommend placing large potted plants or indoor trees, such as ficus trees, in your dad's home or apartment. Especially not if the gentleman grew up on a farm, or spent much time hunting, fishing, or camping. You can imagine why. Too many of these, both real and artificial, have received an unwanted "watering."

We are very fond of tone on tone decorating in this country. Still, an oak chair pulled up to an oak table situated on an oak floor may pose a challenge to someone with dementia. They may not be able to discern the object (chair) from the field (floor). Subtle differences in tone, discernable to us, may not be visible, so the use of contrast can help.

Changes in Language

Aphasia is a term often associated with strokes or other brain injuries. It is a loss of ability to use and process language, and it frequently occurs with dementia.

Aphasia may be expressive and is first noticed when a person has to search for simple, commonly used words. Less understood, it may also be receptive when the person loses the ability to understand the words that are spoken to them.[27] As language skills decrease, body language assumes ever greater importance.

Remember how it felt in your first-grade classroom when the teacher walked around the room? When she paused at your desk, you looked up, maybe worried that you had done something wrong. Then she opened her mouth and literally talked down to you. Even if her words were praise, your heart beat a little faster. She was towering over you, and while you were not quite cowering, you felt the unequal balance of power.

> Be aware of your body position relative to your loved one. If possible, speak eye to eye.

If your family member is seated, this may mean pulling up a chair or even crouching down. If he is sitting, try not to stand directly in front of him or encroach on his personal space. Instead, when standing, position yourself slightly to one side.

Try to stand at no more than a
forty-five-degree angle, remembering those with dementia
may lose peripheral vision.

If you are seated at a ninety-degree angle, say at a dining table, turn your body towards the person when speaking to them. It is fine to sit directly across from someone if there is a table between you. These simple strategies help the person with dementia to feel equal and in control.

Approaching someone from behind
can be very startling, as can an approach directly
from the side. <u>Go slow.</u> Sudden movements can be alarming
as vision is increasingly impaired.

Words may lose their meaning, but tone of voice is always understood. The ability to understand what one is hearing may be lost, but facial expressions, as well as body language, are read. Laughter and music are universal languages.

Wandering (Walking About) — Marilyn

Marilyn was from just outside of Fargo. She had to get back home to the farm. Telling her that the farm had been sold for a housing development simply enraged her. She knew where she needed to be.

Marilyn looked at least fifteen years younger than her seventy-eight years. She had an open and honest face and a friendly manner. Marilyn had lovely clothes. Nursing assistants took care every morning to help her with her hair and makeup. Her daughter had her scheduled for a shampoo and set every week.

Visitors to the memory care community where she lived often mistook her for another family member.

There was a sign at the keypad exit, warning visitors not to allow others to leave with them. Still, visitors could not imagine that this meant someone who looked like Marilyn. She was stopped several times outside of memory care, in the lobby of the retirement community, before she reached the street. A larger, more emphatic sign was made, and one was placed on the outside of the door as well. Still, she managed to convince visitors that a ride was coming to take her to Fargo.

The staff was at its wits' end.

Finally, on a bitterly cold day, there came word that a major winter storm was blowing east into Minnesota from North Dakota. This weather advisory led one of Marilyn's caregivers to have a brainstorm.

She went to the exit door and posted a sign reading, "Blizzard Warning—Highway 2 to Fargo closed." Marilyn went to the door, read the sign, sighed, and walked away. She was from North Dakota, and she knew all about blizzards. There is no going anywhere when one is raging. The storm passed, but the sign stayed up and continued to discourage Marilyn from trying to leave.

Spring arrived, and Marilyn was able to get outdoors and do some gardening in the spacious protected courtyard. Her need to get away subsided. The sign came down. This is an example of what is sometimes called a "therapeutic fib."

And it worked.

Sometimes dementia steals the mind while leaving the body physically fit. Along with dementia often comes a certain restlessness and a need to be in motion. This habit is commonly referred to as "wandering."[28]

Since this "wandering" movement seems to lessen anxiety, it is a good idea to allow for this as best as you can. Some with little space in their home may pace back and forth.

Having an uncluttered floor is vital during this stage.

In a safe and protected environment, wandering should not be a problem. It may be annoying to observers, but it seems to soothe the wanderer. There are occasions when it is much more than an annoyance, however, and may be dangerous.

As discussed earlier, some people with dementia are up at night while their caregivers are sleeping (or attempting to sleep.) Even the most diligent caregiver will have moments when their loved one is unobserved.

While unobserved, a wanderer may decide to leave the safety of their home. Sometimes this is with the intent of "going home," or somewhere else they feel they need to be. Other times, it is simply a desire to keep moving. Lacking self-protective instincts, they may leave without proper footwear or clothing. There are too many stories about individuals going out barefoot in a Minnesota winter. There are cases where patients have flagged down cars and asked for a ride "home," giving their previous, or even childhood, address.

Ask any police officer—most have been involved in returning a wanderer to their home.

I don't mean to frighten you; indeed, not everyone with dementia wanders. But research indicates that the percentage may be more than 60%.[29] The question then is, what do you do if your loved one is a wanderer?

Ask yourself: how secure are the exits of your home, and how willing are you to modify your doors and windows?

How inventive is your loved one when it comes to getting away? And how strong does their passion for escape seem to be? When, and how deeply, does your loved one sleep, and can you sleep when they do? Can you be awake when they are awake? If not, do you have help, or can you consider home health support? How physically fit is your loved one, especially in comparison to you, the caregiver? There are so many variables to consider.

There are times when a move to a secure memory care community with twenty-four-hour awake staffing may be the best option.

It will not eliminate the patient's need to move or attempt to leave, but it reduces opportunities to get away.

An alternative is to have someone with them at all times, alert to their movements.

Unfortunately, this behavior can occur even when the patient is a resident of a care facility. There the term "elopement" is used when someone wanders away. The resident's chart may note that the person "engages in exit seeking."

Most care facilities do their very best to ensure that this doesn't happen. But – people with dementia often look, well, completely normal. Visitors to secure units, accessed only by keypads or by being buzzed in and out, will inadvertently allow a resident to follow them out, *even holding the door for them*. Individuals with dementia can be both inventive and convincing!

> If your loved one does enter a memory care unit, ask what precautions are in place to prevent residents from leaving unescorted.

Many wanderers, however, given enough space to move around, will not try to leave their home environment. They simply must roam. To us, it may seem aimless, but this movement is not without purpose. It meets a need they are not able to articulate.

> Consider installing door alarms, GPS trackers placed in shoes or wristbands, and other innovative technological tools. Don't forget to secure the windows.
>
> You may need to be creative to prevent dangerous wandering. People with dementia can be surprisingly bright and ingenious.

A home is a place where you belong, where everyone and everything is familiar, comfy, and cozy. As memories seep away, even a home of over forty years may seem like a strange place. Your loved one may not feel at home, even in their own house. Wanting to go home, *pleading* to go home, is not unusual.

At times like this, remember that home is where the heart is. Right now, your loved one needs someone to speak to their heart. It may mean a hug, a cup of cocoa, reruns of a favorite TV show. It could mean helping with a homey task, such as setting the table or folding laundry. Your loved one may ask for their mother or their husband. Ask yourself: "Did he look to his mom for comfort when he was sad?" "Did her husband make her feel safe and secure?" Maybe she is feeling lonely and insecure.

> Think about what the person they are looking for meant to them. Then do your best to stand in their stead.

Once they are comforted, try to distract them with a favorite subject, and move on. And yes, obviously, these moments can be very hard on the caregiver. You are doing your best to provide a warm and loving environment, and it is hard when the patient seems to need something or someone else.

This is why you need to be patient and caring with <u>yourself,</u> too.

Hoarding, Hiding, and Thieving — Thelma

As shift was ending, Ashley, a young nursing assistant, approached me, her face screwed up with worry. Her purse was missing!

I asked her where she usually kept it during her workday. She said that she put it safely in one of the kitchen cupboards in the small, open activity kitchen of the memory care community. I watched as realization dawned on her face. Ashely smiled and said, "Thelma!"

She dashed off to Thelma's room and returned shortly with her purse. She found it beneath the pillows on Thelma's bed, all its contents intact. Also under the pillows were several packets of sugar, taken from the dining room. We were used to Thelma's ways. Some people may refer to this kind of behavior as stealing. Another interpretation, however, is that Thelma was simply taking back what she thought was hers in the first place.

Have you ever mislaid your purse? I once set mine down on a department store shelf while looking at sweaters and wandered away without it. My panic was real. I have carried a shoulder bag ever since!

When shopping, dining out, or at any social or cultural event, most of us keep our purses at hand. If we set them down when visiting friends, we note where we left them. When it comes time to depart, we are clutching them to our sides.

> A handbag that is left within reach of someone with dementia is quite likely to be picked up and carried off.

The patient thinks, "Now, where is my purse? Oh, *there* it is!" Thelma never <u>intended</u> to take what wasn't hers.

As for the sugar? Thelma was twelve years old in 1942 when sugar rationing began after the bombing of Pearl Harbor. As a child, she would hoard her portion and wrap it in a handkerchief hidden under her pillow, safe from her many brothers and sisters. In her mind, sugar was still a scarce resource, and she had to hide her share.

Memory care communities sometimes keep a shelf of purses and a hat rack full of men's and women's hats in a common area. The shelf and rack are often empty at the end of the day. That's OK; they are there for residents to take. Staff simply unobtrusively remove them and replace them in the common area each evening.

Confabulation — Peter

I asked Google for a definition of confabulation. It said: "Confabulation is a memory error defined as the production of fabricated, distorted, or misinterpreted memories about oneself or the world, without the conscious intention to deceive." In other words, it is an untruth, but not a lie.

Peter is a gentle giant. He is approachable, generous to a fault, and gregarious. Peter has vascular dementia. In his mid-seventies, this big guy loves spending time at his family cabin. He and his two brothers share equally in the expenses of their lovely lake place, inherited from their parents.

During the summer, the brothers each spend time there with their children and grandchildren. Come hunting season opener, the brothers and their older male offspring claim the cabin for a long "boys' weekend." Hanging above the mantel of the massive stone fireplace is the rack of a twelve-point buck. It is a beauty, perfectly symmetrical.

I stopped in one beautiful summer day and could not help but comment on the trophy. Peter glanced at it proudly and told his story.

"It was so cold that day and the snow was deep. We'd been out since dawn, and hadn't even seen a doe, much less a buck. The coffee was gone, and several of the guys had already packed it in. I'm a stubborn old coot, and I stuck it out. Then along comes the most beautiful animal I have ever seen. I fired off the perfect shot. Man, it was tough getting him back here through the snow."

Behind Peter, and out of his line of sight, his wife is slowly shaking her head back and forth.

Later, she shared that Peter had stayed back in town that weekend, over thirty years ago. There was a severe winter storm that day and the next. Due to the heavy snow, he didn't join the group until Sunday.

Peter's younger brother shot the deer before he arrived.

The story of that particular buck was family lore, and Peter had heard it over and over again. Each time a visitor asked about the trophy, the tale was retold. Peter wasn't trying to take credit for something he hadn't done. He simply heard the story so many times that his brain placed himself smack dab in the middle of it.

Confabulation is a sort of re-creation of history, often with additional frills and flourishes. Sometimes major elements are added or deleted. What confabulation is not—is intentional lying.

> If your loved one engages in confabulation,
> it is usually best not to correct them directly.
> If anyone listening needs to know the truth of the matter,
> you can share it quietly at another time.

It is also interesting to note that we all confabulate to some extent, as you may remember from the description of how memories are formed. My sister and I, who are only a year apart in age, often have dramatically different memories of the same childhood events. We are both sure of our facts, but one of us is wrong. Even healthy brains produce faulty memories.

Denial and the Unreliable Reporter — Sherman

Sherman insisted on visiting his physician alone. The idea that he needed to be accompanied by his daughter was just insulting. He allowed her to transport him to appointments and then left her in the waiting room as he consulted with his doctor.

In Sherman's mind, he was a picture of health.

He remembered to take his pills, slept like a baby, and had no symptoms of any kind. No, he didn't need a refill of medication for indigestion; he had a stomach of iron. He was lucky for a man his age because he had no pain of any kind.

> People with dementia generally experience symptoms well before receiving a diagnosis.

Many of those in the early stages deny the initial symptoms, often as much to themselves as to others. Forgetfulness, poor decision-making, and other effects of the disease are embarrassing and terrifying. Such denial is a defense mechanism and is an understandable psychological response.

As the disease progresses, the connection between the brain and body is gradually degraded.

One of the links that may be severed is that between the conscious mind and the nervous system. This condition has a long fancy name— *anosognosia*. Caused by brain damage, anosognosia may be defined as a lack of recognition of one's condition.[30] Unlike denial, which is psychological, it has a physical cause. The body is not communicating its true status to the brain.

Sherman was what we called an "unreliable reporter" when it came to his health. He claimed to have a stomach of iron, yet eating spicy food, which he craved, inevitably led to excessive gas. He vacillated between diarrhea and constipation. He struggled to stand from sitting and had trouble getting out of bed due to stiffness. Yet Sherman was not lying to his doctor. He was not aware of his own impairments. He was not in denial, and he was not merely forgetful.

Sherman's story is not an unusual one.

People may deny severe pain while they are experiencing it. They do not perceive the symptoms of the bowel obstruction, the urinary tract infection, the swollen joints. Unfortunately, this sometimes results in health emergencies.

Caregivers are often placed in a challenging situation.

Physicians are guided by principles, and one of those is the protection of patient privacy. They may see your patient once or twice a year. Or they may be a specialist meeting your loved one for the first time. Even when treating someone with a diagnosis of dementia, the doctor may be reluctant to go against the patient's wishes if they want to be examined alone.

Deep into dementia, some people can be so persuasive. It can be difficult to insist on being present during an exam.

> Do insist, however, on being present following the physical exam, to share your knowledge with the doctor.

Physicians look for physical manifestations of illness, but they also rely significantly on a verbal description of symptoms. Without the advocacy of caregivers, patients with dementia may not receive the care that they need and deserve.

> It is also important to realize that when someone with dementia acts out, it could be a result of physical pain that he or she is unable to recognize or share.

Facial expressions may provide clues, but sometimes it may be swelling or another noticeable physical symptom. When ill, the patient may also experience symptoms of delirium, including a sudden increase in confusion, anxiety, or anger.

The Body-Mind Connection — Sam

>*Sam was a client of the adult day center I worked in, early in my career. He had severe brain damage due to stroke and suffered from vascular dementia. Sam was confined to a wheelchair and only had the use of his right hand. Fortunately, he was right-handed. He had an artistic flair and an eye for color.*
>
>*We worked together in the ceramics studio. I held the pieces steady as he painted. We chatted about his life, and he shared stories about his family. One day, as he was talking about his beloved grandmother, he looked down at his useless left hand and picked it up with his right. He gazed at me and calmly said, "I loved my grandma, I did. But I never understood why they sewed her arm on me."*
>
>*I was taken aback, but simply shook my head and said, "Well, Sam, some things are hard to understand."*

Sam was experiencing a condition that sometimes occurs with strokes and other types of brain damage, including dementia, in which the patient experiences an inability to recognize familiar objects or people. Sam's case is more striking than most because the stroke caused such significant damage. It was further exacerbated by continued vascular dementia. He failed to recognize a part of his own body. He seemed matter-of-fact about it, not distressed or angry. He was mystified by this arm attached to his side.

Many cases of this kind of disconnect are less dramatic than Sam's.

Your loved one may seem unable to recognize familiar items around the house. He suddenly doesn't know how to use the can opener that you've had for years. Or he may fail to recognize smells or sounds.

If your loved one is startled all out of proportion by the sound of a ringing phone or the doorbell chimes, it may be because she cannot place those sounds. Her brain cannot interpret what she hears.

Adjusting to a New Normal

You may see changes in attention to personal hygiene or appearance, housekeeping, and pet care. Your loved one may sleep much of the day.

Or she may stop a lifelong habit of church attendance and withdraw from events with family and friends. Or he will only eat breakfast cereal, three meals a day.

All these changes may be signs of dementia or depression—or both since they often co-occur.

As dementia progresses, a breakdown in the body-mind connection occurs.

Messages fail to send and receive. Appetite and body temperature sensors seem off. Eyesight and perception change. It is good to name all these changes. While they are not normal, they are well-known and documented.

In dementia, they are not unusual.

CHAPTER 6

IS IT REAL,
OR IS IT MEMOREX?

Real Fidelity

I am using a Memorex flash drive to save my copy as I write—you might be familiar with the brand. Maybe some readers are too young to recognize the old advertising slogan, "Is it real, or is it Memorex?"

It was used to sell cassette tapes, in which the quality was so good, you couldn't tell a taped version from the real thing. People with dementia are often not present in the now. They are living in a "Memorex World."

Reality and memories are fluid anyway. Einstein is quoted as saying, "Reality is merely an illusion, albeit a very persistent one."

The fact is no two people see any situation precisely the same way.

Still, there are certain things that we all agree on to make our society work. These things include the calendar, the clock, and the age of people and things. These markers, which keep our lives in order, are often lost on those with dementia. Our best approach when a loved one is lost in the past is to join them where they are.

Reality Orientation — Clara

Clara was a sweet woman who spent all her days sitting in her chair, humming softly. Sometimes, I would catch a snatch of a song in her mostly tuneless drone. Then I would sing to her, bringing the twitch of a smile to her lips.

I wanted to restore Clara to reality.

We had a Reality Board in the dining room, and I made sure it was always up to date with the current day of the week, day of the month, and season of the year. As often as I had time, I placed Clara's chair near a window and talked to her about what was going on outside.

I pointed to the grass and flowers on the windswept Iowa prairie. Her eyes remained unfocused as she sat impassively and continued to hum.

One day, it began to snow.

As we sat together, I pointed out the white, fluffy accumulation. She turned her eyes to me, nodded, and smiled. I thought I heard her murmur "snow," so softly, I couldn't be sure what I heard. Still, I was thrilled! She saw the world as it was! She connected to reality.

I almost ran to tell the director of nursing, slowing down when I remembered that she would never tolerate running in the calm environment she had created. I reached her in the hall and blurted out my astonishing accomplishment. Experienced and wise, she smiled at me somewhat sadly and moved on. I was deflated, but not discouraged.

Although I volunteered with the elderly during my college years, my first "real" paying job after graduation was as an activity director in a nursing home. I attended a certification class through the state, which at the time was forty hours long.

One of the topics studied was a concept called Reality Orientation.[31] It is a concept still in use in some settings and has some limited positive effects in early-stage dementia.

Now, this was over forty years ago, and little was understood about Alzheimer's disease. Sadly, even today, our medical schools do not cover the subject well.

We did know that following a stroke or other brain injury, if the damage was not too extensive, the brain might reroute its circuits around the damaged area, restoring function. It required intensive therapy and dedication, but success was possible.

So then, why not try to bring this same recovery opportunity to those with Alzheimer's? Let's see if we can fix the broken brain.

The idea behind Reality Orientation was to continually remind the person of today's date, the season, the next holiday. We were convinced that reality is fixed, it is now, and everyone should be on the same page.

"No," we were taught to say, "your mother is not still alive, it is 1975, and she was born in 1870." So we tried, and guess what? If the cognitive impairment was due to a singular vascular incident, sometimes that worked!

At least until the next ischemic attack. Reality Orientation in middle- to late-stage dementia, however, is highly questionable, and often unkind.

As it turns out, I was never able to repeat my "success" with Clara. I continued to reach her by singing softly to her. Still, she never again signaled a response to her outward environment.

I was fighting a losing battle. Her brain was far too damaged.

The progress of the disease would always outpace my efforts. Her brain could not reroute around its broken pieces. The director of nursing understood, through her long experience, what I did not.

> Our version of reality and the reality of a person with moderate to severe dementia is not the same.

Their brain takes in information differently, and it processes it differently. It retains it differently, if at all. They cannot come back to our daily reality, but we can learn to see things the way they do.

We *can* join them in their reality.

A Beautiful Friendship—Frieda and Mabel

The memory care community was designed with a central area that looked like a small town. The beauty/barbershop, the library, and the craft room all had storefront entrances and windows. A circular walking path led past each of these neighborhood "shops." One of the spaces was a private dining room, where meetings were sometimes held.

My colleague Beckie and I were meeting with representatives from the University of Minnesota. We sat together over coffee and doughnuts, discussing a possible research project. Residents passed by on their daily walks.

One pair passed by twice. Frieda and Mabel, both in their eighties, strolled by hand in hand, pausing to wave at us each time. Their third time around, Frieda stopped and tapped gently on the window. Beckie waved them in. As I poured them each a cup of coffee and passed the doughnuts, Beckie noticed their joyful mood.

"You seem happy today. What's your secret?" she asked.

"Oh!" Frieda replied with palpable joy. "I just found out that I'm pregnant!"

Beckie didn't miss a beat. "Do you think it's a boy or a girl?"

Not to be left out, Mabel crowed, "It's a girl!" clapping her hands and smiling from ear to ear.

We all congratulated Frieda. After a few minutes, we gently said that we needed to get on with our meeting. Our guests got up and left.

They strolled away, arm in arm, the best of friends sharing the best of news.

What a perfect opportunity to join with these two lovely women as they relived a happy time, a time of expectation, and great happiness. Their reality was so beautiful.

To be clear, it is always worthwhile to work to maintain whatever capacity is still intact in our loved ones.

In fact, we should all try to build
our mental skills. Learning something new, for instance,
seems to create new neurons in our brains. This may help
build a cognitive reserve, an excess to call on when needed.[32]

So if your dear one loves to play cards, play. If Bridge becomes a "bridge too far," switch to Hearts. If they love jigsaw puzzles, do them. If you need to buy puzzles with fewer and larger pieces over time, do that.

The more resilient and capable our bodies are, the better able we are to respond to the onslaught of any disease. But insisting that someone with dementia experience the reality of today precisely the way that we do is not helpful.

When the capacity to form memory
is lost, new learning is limited.

When the ability to communicate thoughts has been completely eroded, we can focus on reaching our loved ones in another way. Maybe through touch, possibly through smiles. Or like Clara, perhaps through music.

Sometimes, a prayer that has been repeated daily throughout a lifetime, such as a table blessing, will bring a response. It could be a psalm, the Lord's Prayer, a much-loved hymn. A nursery rhyme, a lullaby.

Perhaps, using another sense, it may be the smell of bread baking that elicits a positive reaction. All of these may be meaningful ways to connect with someone about whom we care.

"What day is it?"
"It's today," squeaked Piglet.
"My favorite day," said Pooh.

~ Winnie the Pooh by A.A. Milne ~

CHAPTER 7

WHY THEY DO WHAT THEY DO AND **WHAT WE CAN DO ABOUT IT**

She Just Misses Him—Mary

Mary was always on the move.

Deep into dementia, she was physically strong and active. She lived in a nursing home, in the secured memory care unit.

She carried with her a baby doll. This doll was in her lap at meals, in her bed at night, and in her arms, as she wandered the halls. Helping her to get dressed, brush her teeth, or take a bath was a challenge. She would panic, scream, scratch, and claw to get that doll back in her arms.

Trying to understand, I read deeper into her chart one afternoon. Mary had one child, a son. She put him down for a nap one sunny afternoon. When she went to get him up, he was gone.

She lost her beautiful boy to sudden infant death syndrome.

Mary blamed herself. In Mary's muddled mind, this doll was not a doll. It was her child, a child she was terrified of losing if she ever, ever put him down.

THERE IS OFTEN SOMETHING motivating a troubling behavior. It will help the dementia patient and assist us in providing care if we understand what it is. Often though, those with dementia cannot explain.

So we think back, ask questions, and imagine.

Sometimes well-meaning people can trigger troubling, even frightening behavior. Professionals are not exempt from this. The federal government, together with the state health department, conducts an in-person survey of nursing homes on a roughly annual basis. Infractions are issued, plans of correction must be written, and changes made and verified. This process helps to assure the quality of care.

I met Mary about forty-odd years ago. Inspectors were focused on respect for residents' dignity. That focus, to their credit, continues today.

However, forty-odd years ago, one of their specific tenets regarding dignity was that all activities and care needed to be provided in a manner they deemed "age-appropriate." So in the view of many inspectors, dolls—emphatically and explicitly—were *not* considered age-appropriate to women Mary's age.

When the health department came for a survey, the question among the staff was, "What about Mary?" To Mary, this doll was not just a doll. It was never a plaything. She believed it was her son, and without it, she became frantic, tearful, even aggressive.

Happily, today, realistic dolls are a frequent sight in nursing homes and assisted living complexes. Staff give them to particular residents because they often help to soothe and relax.

Another resident was the mother of eleven children and helped raise several of her grandchildren as well. Rocking babies was her vocation. Holding the beautiful, lifelike doll, we provided calmed and reassured her.

Ain't Misbehavin'—Grandma Anna

My grandmother grew up on a small farm, the eldest daughter in a family with thirteen children. She longed to finish school and become a teacher, but there were just too many responsibilities at home. Then she married young and had children of her own.

But she had grit.

At the age of sixty, after a lifetime of farming and a stint working in a munitions factory during World War II, she went back to school to get her teaching certificate. Grandma taught grade school for several years on a nearby Indian reservation. Long after she retired, when she was in her late nineties, her students stopped by to visit her—a testament to her teaching skill and ability to reach children. She was also a church soloist, strict in her Norwegian Lutheran beliefs, and a stubborn woman with a quick temper. Her anger always blew over quickly, and she had a wry sense of humor.

In short, she was awesome.

In her early nineties and a widow, Grandma left her small farm in northern Minnesota to move into the neighboring town. My uncle retired about then, and he and his wife moved onto the farm. They were her primary support system.

Grandma entered a nursing home at about the age of ninety-six after a fall. She had been dropped off at her little home by a friend after church. Realizing after the car pulled away that she didn't have her key, Grandma thought briefly about walking the half block to her sister's home. Her sister had a spare. But they had argued about something the day before (my great-aunt had a temper too).

So, my feisty, stubborn grandma decided to climb in through her living room window and fell, with disastrous results. Her memory and decision-making capacity were already somewhat impaired. They continued to decline more rapidly after the fall. It was clear that she had some degree of dementia.

I live in the Twin Cities, about a five-hour drive southeast.

One evening after work, I received a phone call from my uncle. He said that the nursing home had called, and they were considering sending Grandma to the nearest large town, about forty miles away, to see a psychiatrist.

As you have read earlier in these pages, I am generally all for seeking the guidance and assistance of specialists.

Still, I asked, "Tell me what is going on." It's a long way to go to visit a specialist. I was concerned that they were looking for a pharmaceutical remedy when a different strategy might work. Medications are sometimes the answer after other options have been considered. In this case, I needed to know more.

Here is the story I heard.

Grandma had always been close friends with a woman living on a farm down the road. Let's call her Velma. Well, Velma's husband, "Leo," was known for his roving eye. And on more than one occasion, he tried flirting with a particular fiery-tempered neighbor.

Grandma was having none of that.

She had no time for Leo and was not shy about letting everyone know it. After Velma passed away, she successfully managed to avoid Leo for years.

Until the day that Leo moved into the same nursing home as Grandma.

Their rooms were not close, but there was no way to avoid coming across each other in the dining room. Concerned, my family let the nursing home know that they should do their best to keep them apart. They also suggested that Grandma be reminded to be polite.

Per family wishes, and in an attempt to forestall issues, before each meal, the nursing assistant reminded Grandma that Leo would be there, and told her she should "be nice."

Then she helped Grandma into her wheelchair, and Grandma grabbed her cane. As she was wheeled down the hall, Grandma waved her cane in the air, yelling, "Let him try to get near me. I'll show him!"

This happened several days in succession before the suggestion was made to visit a psychiatrist. She was causing disruption, and the staff did have to intervene in some way. I'm sorry to say that I was secretly amused imagining the scene, but staff obviously (and rightly) were not.

My family was frankly mortified. I asked my uncle more questions.

"Does Grandma walk?"

"Well, they try to get her up to walk the hall using her walker, but some days she isn't strong enough. They have to walk with her, using one of those belts."

"So, she doesn't use her cane?"

"Well, no, not for a long time."

"Then take it away. Wait until she isn't looking and remove it."

"What if she asks for it?"

"I think she won't. It's just a metal cane, not an heirloom. Remember that she is good at forgetting. If she doesn't see it, it will slip her mind."

Next question from me: "How is Leo looking these days?"

"He has failed. I hardly recognized him."

"Well then, she probably won't either. Plus, her eyesight is worse than yours. I think it would be good if you and the staff stopped talking to Grandma about Leo. Seat them as far apart as you can in the dining *room, and don't remind her about him. Remember that she is good at forgetting and stop reminding her."*

Other issues arose over time, but this problem was resolved with no further intervention.

I want to be clear that the staff of this wonderful facility did <u>nothing wrong</u>. They were working with our family to try to prevent a problem. The actual outcome was the reverse.

When someone with Alzheimer's acts out, trying to correct the individual is not likely to solve the problem.

We have to try to figure out what is causing the reaction in the first place. I suggest using the tried and true "A, B, C" method.[33]

- ○ **A** is the antecedent: What came just before the person reacted badly?
- ○ **B** is the behavior itself: What did the person with dementia do?
- ○ **C** are the consequences.

See if there is a solution utilizing the individual's remaining strengths.

And yes, sometimes being good at forgetting — is a strength.

Looking at Grandma, what happened to cause her angry response? You might think it was Leo moving into the nursing home.

Actually no.

In truth, that was not something she dwelled on or even remembered. No, that was not the antecedent in this case. She reacted when family or a nursing assistant *reminded* her that he was there. And then, adding fuel to the fire, they told this stubborn, feisty woman to "be nice."

Grandma's behavior was distressing to other residents, and the consequences, if she followed through with her threat, were unacceptable.

But if the behavior and possible or actual consequences are the focus, the chances of relieving the situation are slim.

> Understanding what is causing
> the negative reaction, and eliminating the stimulus,
> is the best approach whenever possible.

It is always important to look at the consequences. There are times when loved ones are distressed by "So what?" behaviors. These are behaviors that have no negative consequences for the patient. They may be upsetting to family and sometimes staff, but they are otherwise not a problem.

Let me illustrate with the following story.

Looks Aren't Everything—Stella

Stella came from a solid, middle-class background. She was a housewife who raised her three children in a leafy suburb of the Twin Cities.

A perfectionist, her home was always immaculate, her offspring well-groomed, dinner on time and served on fine china. Stella visited the beauty salon weekly to have her hair done and her nails manicured. Pride in appearance was her hallmark.

She was also a loving, doting mother and grandmother, and her family adored her for all of these attributes.

Stella moved into an assisted living memory care community. She was happy there, making friends and settling into a comfortable routine.

There was only one problem.

Stella had many lovely dresses, suits, blazers, and cardigans hanging in her closet. Yet she insisted on wearing only one outfit—a navy blue tracksuit.

Her daughters were appalled.

They insisted that Stella did not want to dress this way, and assumed that the nursing assistants were making her wear it for their convenience. The staff struggled to get her out of it to wash it. Suggestions that the family buy more similar clothing fell on deaf ears. "You don't know my mom," was the reply.

Finally, Stella's eldest daughter came to the resident services director in tears over her mother's appearance. "You don't understand! My mom wore pearls and heels to vacuum the house. She cooked pot roast in a dress and a frilly apron without getting a drop of gravy on herself. Look at her now! She must be so ashamed!"

Stella was <u>not</u> ashamed.

Stella wanted to be <u>comfortable</u>.

No harmful consequences resulted from her choice of comfy clothing. The daughter's reaction, her dismay at seeing the change in her mother, was the problem. She had always been proud of her immaculate, well-groomed, and chic mom. It was hard for everyone in the family to let go of their image of the mother and grandmother they knew and loved.

Eventually, they came to terms with Stella's new preference, purchased several similar outfits, and everyone was happy. They even found sweatpants and shirts in her favorite colors—hot pink and lime green!

Stella was delighted.

Of course, Stella was still just being Stella, choosing clothing that suited her. What her family found so hurtful was that she was no longer the mother, grandmother, and homemaker they remembered.

It was as if all of the critical roles she played in *their lives* were erased.

Perfectly coiffed, "Grandma Stella" would greet you at the door with a hug, the smell of home-baked cookies, creating a sense of welcome. Stylish "Mom Stella" was always there with just the right words to make everything right when you came home with a bad grade on your math test. Grandma Stella was the first person you called when you failed to get into the college of your choice or didn't get that promotion.

She was a constant source of comfort.

Altering what she liked to wear was an exterior sign of interior change. The anguish that Stella's daughter felt was a painful letting go of the roles her mom had played throughout her life. While other people said, "So what?" when Stella wanted to wear comfy clothes, <u>her daughter's pain was real.</u>

The family grew more comfortable when they realized how delighted Stella was with her hot pink sweatshirt.

Another plus was the fact that with slip-on pants and tops, Stella was able to dress herself. The suits and dresses had zippers, snaps, and buttons that she just could not manage on her own. Needing help getting dressed was hard on Stella's pride. And with three colors to choose from, Stella could decide what she wanted to wear each day.

We all like to be able to make choices.

The ability to make choices is one of the perks of adulthood and an essential component of self-dignity.

As dementia progresses, however, it is vital to limit the number of items from which a person must choose. A long menu at a restaurant can be simply overwhelming to many of us.

If you know what your loved one prefers, it can be helpful to say, "Mom, this place specializes in lasagna, your favorite!"

Offer two blouses to choose from, not a whole closet full. With too many options, your loved one may become frozen with indecision.

Still, their indecision might not stop them from being angry if you make their choices for them!

Of course, there are times when problem-solving, as noted in the examples of Anna and Stella above, will not work. Medication is sometimes necessary to alleviate anxiety and aggression. Sarah, below, is an example.

Anger and Anxiety—Sarah

Sarah, the child of a small-town pastor, lived a sheltered life. She had always been gentle, generous, and kind.

Her daughter, Nancy, the wife of a prominent public figure in the city, wanted the very best for her mom. Nancy took her mom into her own home as Sarah's dementia progressed, and she could no longer live alone.

But Nancy had health problems of her own, children still in college, and many civic obligations. She was losing sleep and becoming depressed. Caring for her mom was a labor of love, but it was increasingly difficult.

Sarah was up at night and slept much of the day. She wouldn't get dressed. Sarah resisted washing her hair, brushing her teeth, and taking her medicine. She became irritable and would yell at her daughter—something unheard of.

At the urging of her husband and children, Nancy evaluated the situation. She realized that she was no longer able to provide the care her mom needed. Sarah was assessed and placed in the memory care community. Nancy visited several times a week and was very involved with her care.

Sarah was restless and anxious. Physically fit, she walked the halls endlessly. It was hard to get her to sit down for a meal.

Staff talked to Nancy about medication to help with her increasing agitation and anger. But Sarah had tried anti-anxiety medications previously, and the family hated how muted, and sleepy they made her. They resisted. When pressed, the answer was a firm, "No!"

Sarah's agitation continued to increase, occasionally flaring into an outburst. Sarah would berate the staff, using vile language, and throwing whatever objects came to hand. If they got too close, she would slap and scratch. Staff tried to understand what caused these catastrophic reactions, but they couldn't identify any specific triggers. They seemed utterly unpredictable. Nancy refused to believe that her minister's daughter mom would behave this way.

When staff shared some specific language her mom used, Nancy replied, "My mother would not use those words. She lived such a sheltered life. She's never even heard those words! You just want her to be easier to manage, to make your life easier. Do your job!"

Then, one day, Nancy came around the corner and witnessed, and heard, her beloved mother in full rant.

Sarah raged, shouted expletives, and physically struck out at a nurse. Nancy suddenly realized that, indeed, her mother was not "being herself." She apologized profusely, and the doctor was able to prescribe an effective medication regime that restored her mother's calm, without "snowing" her.

It is always a difficult question of whether and how much to medicate people for anxiety and agitation. It is doubly hard when an adult is unable to make these decisions for themselves or even share how they feel.

> If you are faced with this kind of situation,
> look clearly at how your loved one is acting,
> and especially at how her actions are affecting others.
>
> Then ask yourself, "How would my mom feel if she could see
> this, and how must she be feeling inside to act this way?"
>
> If she would be distressed and dismayed, the kindest thing
> might be to use the best of medical science to help her.

Catastrophic Reactions

In Sarah's story, I used the term "catastrophic reaction."

What does it mean?

Each person will walk his or her path on the dementia journey. Some experience reactions that seem all out of proportion to the cause, leading to emotional outbursts and even physical violence that seem to come out of nowhere.

Most of us spend our whole lives learning how to manage ourselves. We say things we wish we could take back. We spend more money than we should. We overeat, or stay up too late and regret it the next morning.

When children are young, and they throw tantrums or snatch something without asking, how do we help them? One of the first things we teach our kids is to "use your words."

As those with dementia gradually lose their facility with language, this effective tool may be lost.[34] The tempered language they always employed may be replaced with language you are surprised to hear come out of their mouths. Impulse control may be impaired when the frontal lobe becomes affected, which happens early in some types of dementia and later in others.

How do we protect ourselves and help our loved one when they lash out? I suggest using a process called the Five R's to manage these reactions.[35]

They are:

- **R**emain calm
- **R**espond to feelings
- **R**eassure
- **R**emove
- **R**eturn

When you sense that your loved one is beginning to lose control, it helps if you can **R**emain calm. They sense and respond to your feelings.

Then **R**espond to *their* feelings, validating how they feel. Be careful — telling them that they "shouldn't feel that way" will just result in <u>more anger</u>.

Move on to **R**eassurance, use soothing language, and gentle touch. Remind them that they are safe and give them details about what is going on that may be helpful. Redirect them by talking about something else that is pleasant and comforting, or offer them a favorite food or activity.

If this fails, and the person continues to escalate, you may need to **R**emove yourself a safe distance. Most often, catastrophic reactions blow over quickly.

You may then **R**eturn and carry on with your previous activity.

It is useful, after a catastrophic reaction, to do some detective work, to avoid a similar response.

Remember the ABCs of behavior?

Can you figure out the **A** — the antecedent that may have triggered the outburst? To help in searching for the **A**, use another alliteration. Asking Who, What, Where, and When may help you get to the Why.

Sometimes a particular person or type of dress (maybe a uniform) is an issue. It may be a disturbing sound. Perhaps the mailman appeared and rang the doorbell, the dog barked. It was a cacophony of noise.

It may be something in the physical environment such as too bright lights or shiny, slippery flooring. It could be a difficult topic or a condescending or demeaning approach.

In the case of my grandmother, she was approached in a manner she did not appreciate about a man she did not like. Of course, it is easier to discover the stimulus if the reaction occurs more than once, and you can compare the situations to find a common denominator.

> Just remember that the cause of the reaction <u>does not</u> have to make sense to you.

You know the reaction is unreasonable, at least in the eyes of someone without dementia. Discovering the trigger may help you to avoid future occurrences.

Identifying Triggers—Sadie

The Life Enrichment team worked hard on a Valentine's display featuring wedding photos and other traditional bridal items, including framed gilded invitations, satin shoes, and even a lovely lace veil. They placed the display outside of the dining room on Monday morning, intending to leave it there for the week before the planned Valentine's dinner.

Sadie spent most of her time in her room, puttering about and watching TV, only coming out for meals. She was a quiet and gentle soul, with never a cross word for anyone.

Everyone was startled when Sadie came down for breakfast on Monday.

Seeing the beautiful display, she became enraged. She screamed and tried to tear it down. When a nurse stepped forward and wrapped her arms around her, Sadie began to sob uncontrollably. The nurse led Sadie back to her room and served her breakfast there.

But the same scene was repeated at the next meal. And the next.

- Morning, noon, and evening (**when**).
- Day staff and evening staff (**who**).
- The same dining room where she had eaten three meals a day for over two years (**where**).
- The only difference was the wedding display (**what**).

Staff had to choose between moving the display to another location or serving Sadie all of her meals in her room for a week.

They chose to move it.

Sadie, who had no recollection of her catastrophic reaction, returned to the dining room as usual. The family insisted that Sadie had a long and happy marriage, attended all family weddings, and they all found her behavior inexplicable. But clearly, something about weddings triggered anger and sadness.

Staff correctly identified **what** the antecedent of her reaction was. They discovered the trigger, and the problem was solved.

Sundowning

I always say that God invented the cocktail hour for a good reason.

Evening is a time of transition throughout our lives. Kids come home from school, moms and dads come home from work, evening activities ensue. We are used to doing something different as the sun begins to set.

This is a pattern throughout all of our lives.

It is no wonder that people become agitated as the daylight fades. They feel they should be going somewhere, doing something different.

Don't they have to get home to meet the school bus?

Start dinner?

Is there a game they have to coach?

They don't know what they need to do or where they need to be. But they have a feeling that <u>where they are now is not it.</u>

So they decide they need to go home, or they begin to wonder where their spouse and children are. In the lives of those with dementia, little changes as the day melts into night. How do we help smooth out the transition between daytime and evening routines?

> Difficulties in mood experienced at dusk
> are sometimes referred to as Sundowning or
> the Sundown Syndrome.

For those living in a care setting, late afternoon is also often shift change. Staff are jangling their keys, putting on jackets, calling out "See you tomorrow" to their colleagues. When a patient gets up and moves toward the door, they hear, "You live here! This is your home now."

How confusing!

I imagine someone thinking, "You say this is my home, but you just work here? I can't afford servants!"

How do we help?

> As much as possible, staff in care settings
> should be careful about making a note of their departures.
> For in-home caregivers, it may help to involve the individual
> in setting the table or engage in some other familiar end
> of day activity.

Did mom always love to settle down and watch a little TV at the end of the day? Did dad read the newspaper (it matters little if he absorbs the content)? Offering a familiar evening activity is often helpful.

A Question of Sex — Herb, Clarence, and Maisie

And now a subject that many of us would rather avoid — sex.

Sexuality can be a difficult subject at the best of times. However, we cannot avoid it in our discussion of dementia. Human beings are sexual beings, and while some believe sexual desire declines or disappears with age, that is not always the case.

In my experience, two problematic situations most often arise around sexual behavior. One is the development of a romantic relationship with someone other than a spouse.

> One is the development of a romantic relationship with someone other than a spouse. People with dementia do not always remember that they are married or recognize to whom they are married.
> Another is inappropriate acting out on sexual urges. As the disease affects the frontal lobe of the brain, impulse control is lost, and very fine people may act in extremely objectionable ways.

These issues do not arise in most cases of dementia.

They seem to be relatively rare. Yet they happen often enough that we need to address the topic. No one going through this should feel that they are the only ones. Both of the scenarios described above cause pain, and often shame, to family caregivers.

We do not want to be afraid to let our grandchildren sit on great-grandpa's lap. We do not want to see our wife holding another man's hand.

What can we do?

Herb

Herb was a quiet, gentle, church-going soul. In retirement, he liked mowing the lawn, tending his garden, and bragging about his wife's cooking. He worked hard for forty years as an accountant in a small firm, while raising three kids that were his pride and joy.

Herb was a satisfied man. He was proud of the life that he had built.

But dementia struck, and Herb was changed.

His beloved wife first became concerned when he started using coarse language in front of his grandchildren. This behavior was completely out of character. It escalated from there to suggestive language and even attempted groping.

What do you do if faced with this situation?

First, take steps to protect anyone who may be a victim. Second, a medical evaluation is in order. A dementia clinic or geriatric specialist would be most helpful. Medication may be suggested. If it is decided that your loved one needs assisted living or a nursing home, you may be successful in finding an all-male community.

 Understand that this is the disease, not the person, in action.

It is hard not to feel ashamed, but you know that your loved one is not in control of his behavior.

Clarence and Maisie

Clarence was married for sixty-five wonderful years. He had struggled with memory loss for many years, but his good wife took care of the thinking. She used a wheelchair due to multiple sclerosis. They got on fine—he had the legs, she had the brain, and they lived independently until the day she died.

Clarence moved into assisted living.

And met Maisie.

Like Clarence, Maisie had a long and love-filled marriage. She lived at home with her husband, serving as her caregiver until his health began to fail. She couldn't manage the simplest self-care tasks, was up all night, and he just could not do it anymore.

Maisie moved into assisted living.

And met Clarence.

Neither knew each other's names. He called her "Sweetheart," and she called him, "Dear." Clarence would say, "This is my wife." Maisie would nod.

Maisie's husband was saddened but understood. She still recognized him with a hug and kiss when he visited and clung to his hand. But when he left, she turned to Clarence.

Clarence's daughter had a harder time.

She felt that he was betraying her mom, even though she was gone. Still, she saw the comfort these two brought to one another, so she did not object.

There are times, in situations like this when adult children or spouses simply cannot accept a relationship like Clarence and Maisie's. Staff may then do their best to keep such lovebirds apart, but it is challenging.

In some cases, a move may be necessary
to separate the couple.

People with Alzheimer's disease are still adults, but they are vulnerable adults and may be designated as such by law.[36] They deserve protection from predators, yet they retain the human right to make some choices for themselves.

<u>This is a dilemma</u>, and I encourage
those facing it to seek assistance from a social worker,
counselor, or your faith community.

Note that some behaviors may be interpreted as sexual, and in fact, are not. As mentioned earlier, individuals of both sexes sometimes disrobe in a public area. While this is upsetting to others, the patient is most likely simply trying to be comfortable. They may be hot, or their clothing may be binding or restricting them. It can take some work to find a solution. It may help to find looser items that are more difficult to remove.

The Truth about the Therapeutic Fib — Elmer

Of course, you do not want to be untruthful. There are times, however, when a "fib" is not only kind, it is the only way to avoid causing anguish.

Some professionals disagree with the idea of ever being less than truthful with any patient. Certainly, fabricating elaborate lies is wrong and may backfire. Fibbing, or simply not telling the whole story, however, can be helpful.

Let's look at a couple of examples to demonstrate the difference between the therapeutic fib and a lie.[37]

Suppose your dad passed away sometime after your mom's hippocampus stopped processing life events into memories. She asks you where your dad is. The honest answer is that he died. But each time she hears this, it is the first time. Her grief is fresh, and she weeps uncontrollably. Furthermore, she cannot store this information, and no amount of reminding changes that. Suppose instead; you look at the time when she asks where he is.

"Gee, Mom," you reply, "It's two o'clock on a Tuesday afternoon, where do you think he might be?"

"Silly me, he's at work," or "He's in the fields" or "He's on the golf course," she says.

You say, "I bet you're right, Mom."

Then you distract her from thoughts of your dad with another topic, a cup of coffee, and a cookie.

In addition to looking for people whom they dearly miss, individuals are often looking for two other things: their home and their automobile.

Taking away the car keys is a difficult step. Some people, such as June, who frightened herself by getting lost, relinquish their cars voluntarily. Others fight tooth and nail to keep driving.

One advantage we should not be afraid of using when it comes to protecting someone with Alzheimer's is their ability to forget. They have gotten very good at forgetting.

Elmer

Elmer loved his Oldsmobile. An old steamboat of a car, a nightmare to parallel park, it was the car his son Dale learned to drive in. Elmer kept it polished and clean, but it was always in the shop, and parts were hard to find.

Due to his dementia, Elmer was no longer able to navigate the streets of his small neighborhood. So Dale determined the right thing to do was to take Dad's car to his own home and park it in the extra stall in his garage. When Elmer asked for his Olds, Dale said in all honesty:

"Dad, we had to take it to the garage again."

When Elmer asked when it would be ready, Dale replied, "Well, you know it needs a lot of work, and parts are hard to come by. I can give you a lift if you need to go somewhere, Dad."

"No, that's all right, son, not today, but tomorrow maybe," Elmer would reply.

And he would forget about the topic for a few hours or even days.

Of course, what worked for Elmer won't work for everyone. When it comes to taking away car keys, some families have successfully enlisted the family physician or eye doctor to suggest that it is time.

Occupational therapists can perform professional evaluations to determine whether an individual is safe driving.

In some cases, caregivers have gone farther and disconnected the battery or disabled the vehicle in some way. These big losses cause sadness.

People all want the presence of a loved one, the comfort of being at home, the freedom of the road. The ability to drive signifies adulthood and independence. The presence of your father meant safety and love to your mom. The thought of home means warmth and familiarity.

If we understand what things mean emotionally, we can take steps to provide what they need. A hug, a ride in the country, a visit from a pet, comfort food.

Ask yourself, what did your mom do
to help you when you were upset?

If she sat you on her lap and sang to you, try a hug and music. If she made you a cup of cocoa, make some. These things mean comfort to her.

Reviewing Strategies

The "A, B, C" method looks at the Antecedent (what comes before the undesirable reaction), the Behavior itself (the response you are looking to avoid), and the consequences that result. The goal? To see if you can eliminate or minimize the Antecedent and avoid the Behavior.

To help you discover the Antecedent, it is helpful to use the well-known five W's—Who, What, Where, When, and Why.

- ○ Does the adverse reaction always happen around crowds or a particular person (**Who**)?
- ○ **What** is going on at the time; is it generally during a significant social event, or when it rains?
- ○ **Where** does your loved on react - in the bathroom, in the car in the doctor's office?
- ○ **When?** Is it always morning or early evening?
- ○ Finding the common denominator may help you uncover the **Why**.

As you work on problem-solving, don't forget to evaluate the consequences. If they are minimal, consider ways that you can learn to accept the behavior or reaction.

Sometimes, no matter how hard you try, you can't figure out or predict what causes a negative reaction. They seem to come out of nowhere. At times these reactions may be overwhelming and frightening. In these situations, try to remember the five R's:

- ○ **R**emain calm
- ○ **R**espond to feelings
- ○ **R**eassure
- ○ **R**emove
- ○ **R**eturn

You **remain** calm because your loved one responds to your emotions. You **respond** and validate their feelings because being understood helps to reduce tension. You **reassure** them because it helps them feel safe. You **remove** yourself or other people or objects of their anger for the safety of all. You **return** when the reaction has subsided. These tips may help you in most situations.

However, if your loved one becomes threatening towards you or others, please seek professional help. *This may include calling 911.*

Dementia has many victims. You suffer along with those you care for; it is a given. Yet caring does not include accepting physical violence. You should not live in fear.

Note that the ABCs and the Five R's are in wide use in both education and mental health fields, in addition to dementia care. You may find them useful in other areas of your life as well.

Judicious use of the therapeutic fib can be helpful too.

CHAPTER 8

CAREGIVERS

The Primary Caregiver

Often a spouse or an adult child, the primary caregiver is the person most involved with the patient.

They may live with the individual with dementia or nearby. If this is you, you are generally responsible for making and keeping appointments, managing medications and finances, and dealing with day-to-day concerns.

Primary caregiving can be emotionally exhausting. You are dealing with your own sense of grief and loss, at the same time as providing comfort and encouragement to your loved one. Living with someone who needs constant supervision can be confining and isolating.

This is especially true when other family members and friends are unaware or in denial. Spouses of those with dementia are often reluctant to ask their children for help. I frequently hear: "They have their own lives to live."

But constant stress can bring about a decline in your health, making it difficult to continue providing support to your loved one.

> Please ask for help from family, friends, community supports, and professionals.

The Formal Caregiver

I noted earlier that I am not a medical professional. I am also not a lawyer. So I am not about to offer legal advice.

I will tell you, however, that it is wise to
formalize some decision-making roles in writing before
your decision-making ability is severely impaired.

Elder law attorneys are available to help get your documents in order. They will advise you about several documents to assure that your finances and health care are being managed by someone you trust.

In most communities, there are free or
low-cost services that can also help you.

A straightforward document that it is wise to have in place before your loved one has declined too far to make their wishes known is a "Power of Attorney." Power of attorney forms differ from state to state and are often available on state websites for download.

This power generally gives the individual named the ability to handle finances. Since forms differ between states, if your parent relocates from their home state to be near to you, a power of attorney may need to be redone.

There are life-saving and life-sustaining measures that some people living with serious illness choose to forgo. Ideally, we should all have conversations about such medical interventions *before* a diagnosis of dementia. Still, those in early-stage are often perfectly capable of understanding their choices and giving direction to family members, who can then speak for them.

Some forms allow others to direct the lifesaving measures you do or do not receive if you are unable to speak for yourself. Depending on your state, they may be called a Health Care Declaration, Health Care Proxy/ Surrogate Designation, Advance Directive (aka a "Living Will"), or Durable Power of Attorney for Health Care. These forms are often available for download on state websites. They generally allow you to name someone as a proxy to answer in your stead.

The POLST (Provider Order for Life-Sustaining Treatment) is another document, giving direction to medical professionals. Your health care provider, your attorney, or a social worker will be able to help you access this form if you cannot find it online.

If you are a spouse, you are likely handling both finances and medical decision-making. When there is no spouse, these roles are most often held by close family members.

> It is sometimes recommended, where possible, that these roles be separated—with the daughter managing health care and the son managing finances, for instance. This provides a healthy system of checks and balances.

In a few cases, a trustee may manage finances, or guardian and conservator roles may be necessary. These roles are more formal and require oversight by the courts. Seek the assistance of an attorney if you choose this path.

The Reluctant Caregiver

An acquaintance once said, "Of course you want to care for your mom, she took such good care of you when you were young!" I didn't know how to reply, so I just nodded.

I was silent because — it wasn't true.

I know that some of you who are reading this are also responsible for the care of a family member who may not have earned your devotion. I also realize that sometimes, when a parent has been severely abusive, the only way to protect yourself is to cut off all contact.

If you are reading this book, this is probably not you.

Still, you may be giving far more than you ever received. Or you may be a caregiver by default, simply because there isn't anyone else. The plain blunt fact is: you may be caring for someone that, well, you don't particularly care for.

This book is not intended to be a memoir, although it does contain some family stories. I am getting even more personal here because if you are a reluctant caregiver, you need to know you are not alone.

Due to her chemical dependency and mental health issues when we were young, my mother was not a loving caregiver. She was neglectful at best, abusive at worst.

I have a sister one year older, and a brother two years younger. When we were little and living in St. Paul, Mom worked as a hospital nurse. We had a series of live-in housekeepers, who kept an eye on us kids, cooked, and cleaned. Mom would go to work, come home, and begin to drink.

When I was seven, we moved to a larger home in the suburbs, and there was no more live-in help. At that point, my sister and I assumed responsibilities for cleaning and laundry, and most of the cooking. Due to a history of self-harm and accidents, Mom was not safe to be left alone.

Our dad, who had mental health issues of his own, frequently traveled for work. He often stayed out late when he *was* in town.

I lost count of the parties and events I missed, staying home to "babysit" my mom. Most of my friends were unaware of the reason for my absence. Families of chemical dependents are good at keeping secrets, even lying to conceal them. Our family roles were reversed. The children ran the household and cared for the parents.

The senior year of high school was the worst.

My sister went off to college and didn't come home for Christmas. My brother was only fifteen. Mom and Dad were always fighting, and the drinking escalated. I felt as though it all fell on me.

Fortunately, just before graduation, my aunt and our pastor staged an intervention. Mom began to get her life together after her third stint in residential rehab. I was grateful for her commitment to recovery. Devoted to her twelve-step program, she sponsored others on the path to sobriety. She took a position as a nurse in the same treatment center where she started her lasting road to recovery. She changed lives through her professional and volunteer work. I admired her.

No, she had not been a good parent, but — she became a good person.

We became friends and had a relationship based on who we were as adults and equals. She was a good grandmother to my kids.

We moved on.

Incidentally, if she were still with us, she would happily share all of this with you herself. Her recovery taught her the importance of telling her truth.

As she aged and her health failed, it became clear that I was going to be Mom's advocate and support system. She struggled with cardiopulmonary disease, depression, and early-stage dementia. My sister and brother lived far away. Eldercare was my field of work; I genuinely enjoyed the company of seniors.

I know that I am not making myself look good here, but— I found myself resenting her.

I had to provide her with the kind of care and concern that she failed to give me as a child. I was often irritated and resentful. To top things off, she seldom said thank you and often made excessive demands.

Now, I had devoted my whole career to taking care of other people's parents. I would now take care of mine. Further, I understood that I was teaching the next generation how to treat me when I reached old age. I did accept the responsibility, but I did not like it.

As Mom's health declined, she refused to attend the AA meetings that helped her retain a sense of balance. She needed support, but she rejected it. She snapped at me, and she snapped at my husband. Her rudeness cost her friends, who refused harsh treatment. Her closest friend, and Saturday night dinner companion, passed away. Again, it all fell on my shoulders. It was hard.

I can never thank my husband enough for the support he provided. Our kids stepped up too. But I was *so* irritated by her neediness.

And really, I knew that was *unfair*. Luckily, I got help.

Years earlier, I attended twelve-step meetings—both Al-Anon and Adult Children of Alcoholics—and gained a lot. But this was different. I went to therapy and learned to rebalance our relationship. I grew to understand her limitations and even to laugh when she was at her most self-absorbed. I realized that she loved me as well as she was able to.

I learned to forgive.

I prayed.

I was blessed to be by her side as she took her last breath, and I know that she felt loved. Counseling was my solution, and it worked for me. Your path may be different.

Many have much more to forgive than I did. There are those who, rather than care for a parent who was neglectful or abusive, simply quit. Others provide care while protecting themselves.

 Understand **your** limits.

Sometimes it seems that everyone else comes from a loving household. *Please know that this is not the case.* Others, like you, struggle, not only with the demands of caregiving but with a complicated and challenging relationship.

You are not alone.

Betty

I was working as the activity leader in a nursing home. Betty, who was a wheelchair user, was everyone's favorite. She had the sweetest smile.

She had three children who all lived in town, but she seldom saw them. She missed them terribly. They were always available to take her to the doctor; they made sure that she had everything she needed and paid all of her bills. They sent flowers on her birthday.

But they didn't visit.

She sat alone on holidays.

Just before her care conference, I visited her to invite her to attend. She said that she didn't feel up to it, but could I please ask her children, who would all be present, to come and see her?

I said, "Sure."

At the end of the conference, after the nurse filled the family in on her well-being, I posed the question. There was dead silence in the room. Then the eldest child spoke up. "You know that sweet smile that you all love?" We nodded. "That is the exact expression she wore on her face as she watched our father beat us. So, no, none of us will spend time with her, unless it's necessary. We will see that she receives the best of care, and that's the most we can do."

I learned a powerful lesson that afternoon.

They were providing their mom with *the best that they had to give.*

Yes, some neglect and even abuse their vulnerable parents. Much more needs to be done to protect our elders from abuse. But I learned not to judge people who choose not to spend much time with their parents.

There is often an untold story.

The Long-Distance Caregiver

Many of us have found ourselves in the position of caring for someone who lives hours away. We have many commitments in our own daily lives—jobs, spouses, children, grandchildren, and pets. The list goes on and on.

It is often a struggle to find time for ourselves.

We may not be able to spend time with our loved one, but the responsibility nags at us, causing us to feel those dreaded emotions—guilt and shame. We reassure ourselves, and others reassure us that we have our own lives to live. But still, we fret and ask, "Should I be doing more?"

The **more** we travel to be with our loved one — the more we feel that we are dropping the ball at home. The **less** frequent our visits, the more we feel that we are letting our loved one down. No one solution will lead to the perfect balance for you and your family.

But realize this: you <u>do not</u> have to be the one to provide all of the answers.

There are services available to assist you.

If your mom doesn't have family living near her to provide help and support, consider seeking assistance. And if your mom does have family living near her, you may still want to consider seeking help. That help may come in the form of physical, emotional, or financial assistance, or all of the above.

It is essential to do our best to refrain from judging the family that is "on point."

A common issue is a disagreement between siblings. Remember that when we feel guilty about what we are unable to do ourselves, we sometimes feel anger towards others that we feel are not doing enough.

Direct caregivers can be very frustrated and hurt when other family members swoop into town for their biannual visit and determine that immediate changes need to happen. While it is certainly possible that they do, remember that the primary caregiver is closer to the situation.

If you only see mom twice a year, you may be missing pieces.

On the flip side, if you haven't seen mom in a while, be careful not to dismiss or diminish the concerns of the immediate caregiver.

> Unless you are on point, you may not understand how taxing caring for mom may be.

Yes, even if mom is living in assisted living or a nursing home, there are significant demands.

Decision Points

There are many points along the dementia journey when the patient and / or the caregiver must make a significant decision. Between these significant crossroads, there are turnings when additional decisions must be made.

These can be the most disturbing moments:
- when to seek a diagnosis
- when to add home care services
- when to consider another living situation
- when to turn to hospice or palliative care
- and on and on

Each of these turning points comes with another set of questions for the caregiver. Here is just a simple sample:
- How do you take care of yourself along the way?
- If you choose to care for your husband at home, how do you lift someone heavier than you are?
- When a lack of sleep and skyrocketing blood pressure threaten your health, how do you manage?

It's easy to find people who tell you to take care of yourself. I see a different quote on Facebook every day.

But — it is way harder to find people who will step in to offer reliable support.

If you are a spouse, you are dealing with guilt. If you have children, they are likely dealing with guilt all their own, which may influence their advice. If you are a friend or a nephew, caring for a childless elder, you may wonder where your limits are.

You feel pressure from all sides to "do the right thing," but you don't know what that is. And those you count on for support may have different ideas about how to proceed.

You feel lost and lonely.

The closest caregiver, often living with the patient or seeing them many times a week, usually has the best understanding of how far the dementia has progressed. But—and this is a **big but**—sometimes the direct caregiver can be so used to accommodating ongoing change that they don't realize how serious the damage *is*.

Like the story of the boiled frog: the warm water feels fine, and the frog does not notice the gradual increase in temperature until it is too late to jump out.

When it comes to these crossroads, if you do not already have a support system, including professional assistance, please seek it out.

If your doctor is not versed in dementia (and many are not), ask for a referral to someone with this expertise.

If your finances are limited, there are county and not-for-profit social services organizations that can help.

Your local Alzheimer's Association is one source of help and referral.

Reaching Family Consensus

Many of the topics in this chapter have to do with decision points, such as:

- ○ When is dad no longer safe to live at home?
- ○ When is it no longer safe for mom to live alone with dad?
- ○ When should we take the car keys away?
- ○ Should we consider home care services?
- ○ Housekeeping assistance?

- ○ "Meals on Wheels"?
- ○ An emergency pendant?

It is at these moments when we are most likely to disagree.

Differences of opinion may surface between the spouse and the children and between siblings. Making matters more sensitive, financial issues overlay health and safety concerns.

> Blended families often face
> particular challenges.

When family members see things differently — assuming that everyone has the patient's best interest at heart — there are some simple rules I suggest keeping in mind:

- ○ The primary caregiver has the most current and immediate information about the patient's needs and capacity. They deserve respect and appreciation.
- ○ The primary caregiver, being human, can only do so much. He or she may be unable to admit to or fully understand their loved one's needs. He or she may not recognize their limitations.
- ○ Regardless of the primary caregiver's limits, the specific needs of the patient must be met
- ○ Other secondary caregivers and family members have the right and responsibility to raise concerns about gaps in care without fear of alienating the primary caregiver.

Understand that if I am the primary caregiver, and you suggest that dad isn't safe in my care, I may feel shame and fight back. I will be defensive and resist help, even when getting assistance is in my own best interest.

> Do your best to discuss issues
> without blame. Recognize that everyone has a stake
> in the well-being of your loved one.

There may be a family member who stands apart, saying that they just can't bear to see mom this way. Others may check out and refuse to participate in any way. Though it is hard to accept, we all have limits, emotional, physical, and mental. You may have to adjust your expectations.

> Do your best to keep everyone informed
> and keep the door open for support when it comes.

Some primary caregivers feel that asking for support or assistance is a failure on their part. Other family members are afraid to rock the boat by suggesting that mom needs more help than she is getting.

These are natural tensions and normal family dynamics. *They can be challenging to navigate in a family that communicates well.* If the family is dysfunctional, things can escalate quickly. In many communities, there are social service and mediation services available to assist you.

You are not alone.

Safety and Security vs. Freedom and Independence — Simon

At times like these, we are influenced by our values. Unfortunately, our values may conflict. This conflict may be internal, or it may be with other loved ones or professionals. Two values often opposed in these decisions are independence/freedom versus safety/security. Some examples include:

○ Mom is not safe on the roads, but taking away those car keys will limit her ability to get out and be independent.

○ Dad is deteriorating rapidly and wandered away from home twice in the last month, once having to be returned by the police. He should be in a more protective environment or have live-in help. But he would hate moving. He would hate having someone telling him what to do in his own home.

○ One sibling feels that remaining at home is the most essential thing in the world. Another can't sleep at night and just wants to know that dad is safe.

Nobody is "wrong" here. It's a question of what each person feels is of the highest importance.

> Acknowledging the validity of each person's viewpoint is an excellent first step.

No one wants mom or dad to feel limited, and no one wants mom or dad to be at risk. Navigating the way to a decision is more manageable when everyone understands the other's good intentions. No one can tell you exactly when to make a change, even when all agree that change is inevitable.

> When making choices, be mindful of the risks and responsibilities the primary caregiver will bear — because of your decision.

When a spouse is a direct caregiver, he or she often covers up the level of disability of their spouse, whether intentionally or simply out of a lifelong habit of interdependence.

It is not unusual for the caregiving spouse to experience a health emergency.

When other family members step in to assist at home, they sometimes find a level of confusion and forgetfulness that goes well beyond what they had ever imagined. They may be surprised to find that their parent cannot be left alone safely, even momentarily.

There is a point at which outsiders may step in if they feel that the risks assumed are too great. The police, when returning dad home for the third time, are likely to contact County Adult Protection. A neighbor may report a situation they feel to be unsafe.

> It is certainly best to make a decision before the opportunity is taken out of your hands.

Simon

Simon had always been a go-getter. A retired salesman, he never met a man (or woman) he didn't like. Not one to sit at home, he was always on the run.

After a series of strokes, he began to experience dementia symptoms. His legs were so weak he could no longer operate the gas and brake pedals in his car. Reluctantly, he agreed to give up his Ford.

But he got out every day.

Simon had a motorized cart that he took to the little general store and coffee shop on the corner. The owners looked forward to seeing him daily. One day, out of the blue, Simon heard from his college roommate Stan. He just happened to be in town, and he gave Simon a call. "Hey, buddy," he said, "how about meeting for a burger and beer at our old stomping grounds in Dinkytown?"

Now, these old friends hadn't been in touch for a couple of years, and Stan didn't know about the strokes. Simon didn't want to let his pal down, and he didn't want to ask for help.

The police were called when someone reported — a motorized wheelchair entering the ramp to Interstate 35.

Simon's fierce independence, which was widely admired, and his safety came into serious conflict. Limits had to be placed on his freedom. It was frustrating and inconvenient for all concerned, but his days of freewheeling solo excursions had to be curtailed.

The Imperfect Caregiver

This is all of us.

We all have limits.

We need sleep, but we are often deprived of it. We need time alone, but there isn't any. Some days are tough, and some are better—but every day is unpredictable. We are tired and stressed, and sometimes it shows.

Other people try to be supportive, but they are so busy with their own lives, we feel alone. So sometimes we snap at our loved one. We are impatient. We say things that we wish we could take back. We feel bad about the way we are doing the good work of caregiving.

The first thing we must do is learn to forgive ourselves, be kind to ourselves.

We are human, and therefore imperfect. Caregiving is exhausting and frays the nerves. We will not be perfect, and that is OK.

Second, we must seek help so we can find some time to refresh ourselves—a support group meeting, an afternoon of shopping, or even the chance to sit down alone for a moment with a cup of coffee and a good book.

America is a nation of volunteers. Most of us are ready and willing to jump in and help others in need. Paradoxically, we are extremely reluctant to ask for help when we need it.

We recently lost our neighbors, a lovely couple from Ukraine, who passed away in their nineties. Thanks to them, we enjoyed many an excellent dinner of homemade borscht. While they were still here, each snowy morning, my husband and our neighbor across the street would race to see who would be first to clear their driveway. They did this without being asked because—I assure you—the request would never have come. It was up to us to recognize their need and step in.

As caregivers, though, we should not rely on others to help without being asked.

We need to overcome this strange need to manage everything on our own. **Do** call on friends, family, community resources, and professional support to get the relief that you need.

The Stand-by Caregiver

Some caregivers are watching from the sidelines, waiting for the other shoe to drop. They feel helpless, wondering if and when to step in.

Maybe dad is taking care of mom. He is faithful and true to his promises. He remembers the line from his wedding vows "in sickness and in health." So he remains responsible for every detail of his wife's care.

Their daughter stands by.

She worries about mom, yes, but worries about dad even more. There are many variations of the stand-by caregiver. Some don't consider themselves caregivers at all.

But they are.

They are in a constant state of watchfulness, and the stress is real.

All of the Above

Some of us just seem born to be caregivers.

I have played each of these roles over the years with various family members. At one point, I simultaneously juggled several of these different sets of responsibilities. And worked full-time while managing a household.

I was very blessed because I had an understanding employer and flexibility with my job. I did ask for and received support and encouragement. My best friend, who is also my husband, carried the load along with me. I've lost track of how many times and ways I have stated this in these pages: SEEK HELP. A wise friend once said to me: "Angie, you don't ask, you don't get."

ASK.

The Greedy Caregiver

I would be remiss not to bring this up.

Most caregivers give up hours, days, weeks, and years of their lives, selflessly taking care of their elder family members. Yet, it is essential to remember that people with dementia are incredibly vulnerable.

Some caregivers are not acting in their family member's best interest. Some go beyond financial abuse and engage in physical or emotional abuse. You may have read about such cases in the newspaper, or seen stories on TV—cases where the caregiver deprives the elder of necessities and spends their resources on themselves.

State and local governments are getting more serious about cracking down in such situations.

If you are concerned about
a caregiver who is taking advantage of an elder,
please <u>contact authorities</u>. This may mean a call to
Adult Protection — or the police. Do it.

CHAPTER 9

GIFTS AND GOOD TIMES

Remaining Skills — Richard

Richard was a retired high school chemistry teacher. He loved everything about his chosen profession and hated to retire. Although he never missed a beat in the classroom, teaching the subject he held dear to his heart since his high school years, he forgot other essential aspects of his job.

Finally, reluctantly, he hung up his lab coat for the last time and said goodbye to his colleagues and beloved students.

Not long after that, he lost his devoted wife.

His children soon realized that he was no longer able to care for himself. He moved into assisted living. He seemed to lose interest in all of the things that used to bring him joy, playing cards with friends, telling tall tales, even food.

Then one day, the Life Enrichment director, who was setting up an inter-generational program with the local high school, approached him with an idea. How would he like to tutor a few chemistry students? It was a risky, bold idea. Would he be able to do it? Armed with a textbook, he decided to give it a go.

To everyone's joy, the tutoring experience was a blazing success for all involved.

One of the ways to honor those who have dementia is to see and appreciate their remaining strengths. Ella, whose story began this book, is my favorite example. She sensed the discomfort of others and used her gift of music to ease the tension in that elevator.

Ella (Reprise)

About five years after our elevator sing-along, I reencountered Ella.

She had moved to a nursing home dementia care unit. She was no longer able to walk. Over time, she had forgotten her married last name, then her maiden name. Still, she responded to Ella, with the same bright smile.

Her attempts at conversation were strings of garbled syllables. I had low expectations when I arrived with my guitar and sat down to lead a hymn-sing. Her eyes were downcast, and she appeared to be sleeping. I launched into an old favorite of hers: "Amazing Grace."

Suddenly alert, she raised her head, looked into my eyes, and in perfect time belted out four verses without missing a note or a word.

Perhaps you can think of a time when your loved one, even in the depths of dementia, used their wit, their artistic ability, or simply their loving smile to bring joy or comfort to others. We concentrate so often on what the patient has lost that we may miss the chance to appreciate what they have kept. They may have an exquisite sense of timing as they tell that joke for the one-thousandth time. They may be able to sing, to dance. Music seems to be a language that can be shared even when a normal conversation is no longer possible.

Organizations have formed choirs, dance groups, storytelling groups, and drumming circles with wonderful results. There are sometimes latent abilities waiting to be discovered.

Classes in the visual arts may be an entree to undiscovered artistic talent. Dementia patients have created stunning drawings and paintings, amazing their friends and family. Whether they were discouraged from creative expression or inhibited earlier in life, we don't know. Still, their talent has found new expression in their illness.

In many cities, art museums, universities, and colleges offer special classes and tours for dementia patients.

People sometimes retain more skills than we realize. For each of us, a sense of purpose is important. Whether it is helping to set the table, rocking a baby, or doing simple woodworking, having something useful to do is good.

Remembering and Reminiscing — Leona (Mom)

My mother and uncles grew up on a farm in northwest Minnesota. It is an area of austere beauty, full of wildlife and majestic pines. Immigrant Norwegians and Swedes mainly settled it, used to cold winters, hot summers, and hard work.

During WWII, my grandparents sold their farm and relocated to the Twin Cities. They worked for a time in the munitions factory helping the war effort. After WWII, they moved back north and bought a small farm a mile or two east of the old one. It boasted a small modern barn with a hayloft where our cousins enjoyed playing.

Mom went up to visit every year for Memorial Day weekend.

One year, driving the same route that she had taken for all her life, she got lost on her way to her hometown. She still wanted to make the trek "up home" every year, but we were nervous about her going alone.

So for the next several years, I went with her. It was a time to connect with family. I also loved spending time in a place that— though I never lived there—still feels like home to me. On our way into town, we would pass the old farmstead where Mom grew up.

One day she pointed to the big red barn and said, "I remember when my dad and brothers built that barn!" I asked her to tell me more. She did not need much encouragement to talk about the old-fashioned barn raising, the neighbors all pitching in to get the walls and roof built. In keeping with tradition, after a barn was built, the homesteaders would hold a barn dance to thank everyone who helped. Mom was only fourteen, and she was not allowed to go to parties or dances. Well, they couldn't keep her away this time, not when the party was right there on the farm!

How her eyes shone when she talked about that night, what she wore, and the fun she had. I might have never learned this lovely piece of family history if I hadn't prompted her.

I still smile at the gift of this story.

Are you embarrassed when you do not remember something that you know you should? Something someone shared with you when you weren't listening, so maybe you never stored it in your memory. Or it might be a name that is on the tip of your tongue. It is information you know you have, but you just can't manage to retrieve it when you want it.

Frankly, I feel stupid when this happens to me. And nobody likes to feel stupid.

Asking someone with memory loss to recall information that is out of reach is not fruitful, nor is it kind. They may have lost the ability to store the memory, or the area of the brain where it is stored may be inaccessible or impaired.

Whatever the reason, we know that querying people who struggle with forgetting can lead to unhappiness or even anger. Be careful.

But—and this is a big but—it is so rewarding to sit and reminisce about the more distant past.

Since the recall of recent events is often the first thing lost in Alzheimer's disease, we sometimes forget to spend time remembering with our loved ones. A memory of the distant past often remains late into the disease process. For many loved ones, what a past it was! Speakeasies, the Great Depression, World Wars. Women are getting the right to vote. The Civil Rights Movement, the Kennedy Era, man's first walk on the moon. And, closer to home, the family farm, the cabin on Long Lake, making dill pickles and maybe even moonshine!

Every person has little pieces of history to share that bring the past to life for us.

There may come a time when all of your loved one's recollections are lost. *Ask while you have the time.*

Ask about the one-room schoolhouse, about walking miles to school uphill (both ways, with only a single potato in their pocket to keep their hands warm, and they later ate the potato for a grateful lunch).

If your mom grew up in the city, ask about riding the streetcar, playing jump rope or hopscotch on the sidewalk. Your loved one will enjoy it, and you will too.

Finding Purpose — Joanne and Doris

The memory care unit was built in a quadrangle. In the center were offices and a serving kitchen. Twelve resident rooms were located on the outside of three corridors. The fourth side held a common living room and a dining room.

Joanne was a retired registered nurse. She had been the head nurse on the maternity wing of a small hospital in rural Minnesota. Like most RNs, during her career, she spent much of her time doing paperwork. Her standard work practice was to do rounds each morning and afternoon.

Joanne did not recognize that she had dementia.

She believed that the memory care nurses were under her supervision. Each morning, she would rise, don her lab coat, sling a stethoscope around her neck, and do rounds. She walked slowly around the small community three times in succession, stopping to take a pulse, feel a forehead, chat with a resident. She might stop a nursing assistant to offer a suggestion. When rounds were completed each morning, she joined the other residents in meals and activities until the evening, when she resumed her "responsibilities."

Joanne never interfered with the staff's performance of their duties, and she felt purposeful and happy.

Doris was in later stages of dementia. Confined to a wheelchair and unresponsive to her environment, she was often engaged in repetitive behavior. These behaviors are not uncommon in later-stage dementia, and may involve constant tapping on a flat surface, or repeating a single word or phrase over and over.[38] In Doris's case, this involved clapping. Doris sat in the dining room much of the day, clapping, clapping, clapping. The cadence was always the same: clap, clap, clap, rest, clap, clap, clap, rest.

One morning, as Joanne did her rounds, she took particular note of Doris.

She passed her once, then twice. As she circled past Doris for the third time, she reached out and gently put her hand on the arm of a passing nurse. She nodded at Doris. "Now that," she said very quietly, "that is the worst case of the clap I have ever seen." The nurse's mouth dropped open as she began to giggle. Joanne simply winked, chuckled to herself, and continued on her way.

Joanne knew perfectly well that she was making a joke and an amusing one! She remained professional, making sure that Doris or other residents did not overhear her. The humor, care, and compassion she used throughout her nursing career brought comfort to other residents and joy to the caregivers.

Joanne's career was such an integral part of her life, leaving it behind was near to impossible. A nurse was not just what she was, but who she was. Continuing her "work" allowed her to feel happy and fulfilled.

In other situations: a wife sets up a drafting table for her architect husband; a son uses a spare bedroom to create an office with accounting journals on the desk for his dad, who had owned an accounting firm.

> The quality and quantity of the work they complete aren't what matters. Feeling productive *does*.

We are a nation of worker bees. A gentleman once said, "My mom worked her fingers to the bone all her life. It's time for her to sit and relax." His problem was, she kept asking to help with the dishes and the laundry.

The advice, of course, was to let her help. The activity lessened her stress and restored a sense of normalcy to her life.

CHAPTER 10

RESOURCES AND SUPPORT, **PART 2**

Assisted Living

A general principle when it comes to any individual living with any chronic illness is that they should be allowed to live in the least restrictive environment possible. That typically means living independently in their own home or private apartment, with or without supportive services. In many cases, however, an alternative setting must be considered.

I would love to give you a thorough and complete understanding of what assisted living has to offer, but I simply can't.

Assisted living is primarily state-regulated. I have been involved in providing or arranging for assisted living services in four states: Minnesota, Iowa, Wisconsin, and Florida, and I had to learn different rules in each location. Each state differs from the others in terms of levels of care they allow or require providers to offer. You may find settings, for instance, where staff cannot give injections of insulin. Others limit the number of hours of hands-on care an individual can receive.

> It is vital to be a good consumer advocate
> in choosing **assisted living**.

There are several common denominators.

In these settings, you will receive housing in the form of a studio or one-bedroom suite. More rarely, two-bedroom apartments are available.

In some cases, rooms are shared by two occupants. Meals, housekeeping, and some social activities are generally included.

Above that, you will typically choose from services including (but not limited to):

- ○ Laundry services
- ○ Assistance with dressing and grooming
- ○ Assistance with transferring (from a chair to a wheelchair, on and off the toilet, etc.)
- ○ Assistance with setting up medications
- ○ Reminders for taking medications

These services may be offered bundled into a package or offered a la carte. The provider generally determines how to bill for services. Assisted living is commonly private pay.

Some long-term care policies do
cover assisted living.
For low-income individuals, there are state/federal assistance
programs that cover some costs if you qualify.

That said, in many states, providers are not required to participate in these subsidy programs, and residents can be required to move if they can no longer afford housing and service costs.

Even if your loved one has
the resources to cover their stay in assisted living,
for the time being, it is worth asking whether state or
federal subsidies are accepted if funds run out.

Moving

It can be difficult for a person with dementia to move to a new location.

Even deep in the disease process, many people can find their way around in their own home. A move may cause confusion and upset.

Yet there are times when for the safety of the individual or the wellbeing of others, a move is necessary. Often, those of us who have been involved in recommending such a move run into strong opposition from loved ones.

The decision to move is fraught with anxiety. Once made however, things often turn out much better than expected.

Alice

A recent widow, Alice lived alone in the large suburban two-story home where she raised her three kids.

They were the first family to move into their new development, over fifty years ago. Alice had always felt that it was her job to welcome everyone. Years passed, and neighbors aged along with the homes. Many chose to downsize and moved away.

Still, Alice was the neighborhood grandma, bringing fresh-baked pies to new neighbors and watching small children while their mothers ran errands. She played bridge, entertained, and enjoyed many friends.

Then people began to notice changes, subtle at first, and later more apparent. Her house wasn't too clean, and neither was she. She couldn't seem to remember the simplest things.

Her daughter took her for an evaluation, and Alzheimer's was diagnosed. As her dementia increased, she was no longer invited to play cards, and her mistakes in the kitchen led to friends declining her invitations. Young moms realized that she couldn't keep an eye on little ones, even for a few minutes.

Alice felt shunned and purposeless.

The family conferred with one another and decided that a move to an independent senior apartment was inevitable.

To their surprise, Alice did not object.

The family was stunned when the resident services director suggested that memory care would be more appropriate. Alice's doctor concurred with this recommendation. Alice's kids were not convinced and agonized over the decision, afraid that living with "those people" (some more afflicted than Alice) would depress her. Eventually, they decided to try it. Alice took possession of her studio apartment on Memorial Day weekend.

Her daughter, completely stressed out, went away for a few days.

Returning after the long weekend, she visited her mom, filled with trepidation. She said to Alice, "Mom, you can tell me the truth, how do you like it here?" She was amazed when Alice beamed and said, "Oh, I love it! I'm not stupid here."

This touching story reminds us that *people with dementia know that they are adults and have expectations for themselves. Often, when they see the expressions on the faces of others and realize that they cannot meet the expectations of them or society, they are ashamed.*

Worse than that, the people that they relied on for friendship are deserting them—they are being "unfriended."

Living in a supportive environment, with expectations that can be met, can be so freeing.

Unfriending

Why do many older people avoid their friends with dementia, sometimes seeming to "unfriend" them?

I think that the simple answer is fear.

They are afraid that they are going to suffer the same loss, and they cannot face it. So they disconnect. The person being shunned feels shame: "When I feel that I don't measure up to what my family, friends, and society as a whole expect of me, I am crestfallen."

The internal conversation continues, "And if there is no way for me to be better? If I can only expect to continue to disappoint? I may put enormous pressure on myself, or I may give up."

How do we help someone caught in this lose-lose situation?

Well—what do we do for people who lose the ability to walk and use a wheelchair to get around? We remove obstacles that impede their mobility, or we find another route. How do we help them up the steps? We build a ramp. We do our best to create an environment that provides support; *we remove barriers.*

What does this mean for someone with dementia?

> The answer will be different in every case.
> Mostly, it means not expecting what we know we can't get.
>
> We do not expect the retired concert pianist with severe, debilitating arthritis to play Chopin.
>
> We should not expect someone with severe memory loss to remember.

We provide environmental cues, reminders, and encouragement. We ask our loved one to remember the distant past, happy memories that are still retained. *We don't ask them to remember their doctor's appointment.* We do this even though we are sad, and maybe even frustrated.

We may realize that we need a support group or counseling for ourselves because our feelings do count too.

We do our best to offer our loved one the chance to live in a supportive environment, where expectations can be met.

Assisted Living Memory Care

Many assisted living communities offer two living situations: traditional assisted living and memory care assisted living.

Many individuals with dementia do fine in traditional settings, where they are prompted to go to meals and activities, reminded to take their medications, and otherwise supported.

Sometimes, however, the disease is advanced to the point that a transfer to memory care is recommended. Memory care communities typically have a secured entry/exit to minimize wandering. They may also be smaller, with fewer suites or apartments, and have a higher staffing level.

Annie

Annie was living in a one-bedroom apartment in an assisted living community. She became increasingly restless as her dementia progressed. She spent her time roaming the halls. She believed that the community she lived in was her home, and her neighbors were her guests.

Despite pleading from management, many of her neighbors left their apartment doors unlocked as they spent much of their day in the dining and activity rooms. One day, a neighbor returned to her room to find Annie standing at her sink, rinsing some dishes. She insisted she was in her own home, and they were her dishes.

Another time, a gentleman returned home to find Annie sound asleep on his couch. Small items began to disappear from common areas and other residents' rooms. When things were retrieved from Annie's apartment, she argued that these were her possessions, and she genuinely believed it.

She was adamant and angry.

The other residents began to avoid her. She often dined at a table alone.

A naturally outgoing person, she was increasingly isolated.

The resident services director brought all of these issues up to Annie's children. She recommended a move to a setting where there would be more staff supervision and possibly fewer temptations for Annie. An opening in memory care was available. It would mean a roommate for Annie, less space, and perhaps hardest of all, a move. Family members were sure that this would be devastating to Annie. But Annie's increasing needs, and her continued violation of the rights of her neighbors, meant that a change was necessary.

The family very reluctantly agreed.

They moved Annie on Saturday.

When I arrived on Monday and asked how Annie was doing, the resident services director responded with a big grin. "Great!" she replied. "Annie and her roommate, Martha, took one look at one another and decided that they were sisters, sharing a bedroom."

Annie and Martha were comfortable with one another. They spoke the same language, understanding each other even as their language skills deteriorated. They shared their possessions, as sisters often do, and they thrived.

Now, of course, not every move goes this smoothly.

Some struggle to adjust. Still, I must say that many, many family members have repeated this line: "Our only regret is that we didn't do this sooner."

Long-Term Care Center
(aka Skilled Nursing Home)

I would like to address a couple of misconceptions that people have about nursing homes.

First, caregivers do not simply decide to "put" someone without significant needs in a nursing home. An estimated 65% of nursing home residents participate in Medical Assistance (Medicaid). The vast majority of nursing homes accept federal funds and are required to submit a lengthy document detailing the level of services required by an incoming resident.

The average nursing home resident receives 3.7 hours of direct nursing services per day.[39] Federal and state governments do not want to pay for such a high level of care if a less costly alternative is available. If a potential resident does not need enough care, they may not qualify. Even after they move in, if their needs drop significantly, they may be asked to move out. Do be assured, however, that those requiring 24-hour supervision will most usually meet the test.

Second—many mistakenly believe that nursing home care is paid primarily by Medicare. Medicare covers nursing home care only in restricted circumstances and then only for a limited period. These nursing home stays are usually for a short period of rehabilitation or recuperation.

Longer-term nursing home care is primarily paid for privately, or through long-term care insurance (which many individuals do not carry). When private resources are extremely low, the resident's monthly income continues to be paid to the facility, and the balance of costs is subsidized through Medical Assistance (aka Medicaid).

Nursing homes are still a destination for those who need a great deal of supervision or care. They are a critical element in the continuum of care settings. There will always be people who need several hours of hands-on nursing assistance every day.

Many nursing homes today work hard to provide a homey and comfortable environment, offering more privacy and personal touches than in the past. Competent and caring providers do their best to create an atmosphere where people live out their days in comfort. The staff that I know who work in these care centers are uniformly loving and skilled.

If your loved one does need nursing home care,
either long or short term, visit several and listen carefully to
recommendations from family, neighbors, and friends.

There are nursing home level memory care settings, as well. The federal government issues five-star ratings so you can compare quality. You may also be able to access a state website and review the deficiencies found on each facility's most recent survey. It is the job of state and federal surveyors to find and cite any errors nursing homes make. It is indeed rare for a nursing home to have a deficiency-free survey. Employees of nursing homes who receive one celebrate the way a baseball team celebrates a no-hitter.

Don't be discouraged by a few deficiencies,
but instead look for a nursing home that has fewer
deficiencies. Deficiencies can be for minor infractions or
significant flaws.
They are cited by level, so you can see which facilities have
more serious or care-related issues.

A word about professional caregivers is warranted.

We are all born with individual talents and capabilities. When we talk about talent, we are often referring to athletic ability, musical gifts, academic excellence, even business acumen. A less considered expertise—a rare one and not highly regarded—is the ability to care for those who are frail and elderly.

I can attest to the fact that many professional caregivers consider their occupation to be a calling. Motivated by love and a deep appreciation of our elders, they work patiently and gently to provide the best care they possibly can.

Professional caregivers can accept the patient with dementia just the way they are. No, they will never love your family member the way you do. On the other hand, they do not face loss and grief each time the patient fails to accomplish simple tasks or cannot remember their name. Professional caregivers play an important role in the caregiving landscape.

CHAPTER 11

LATE STAGE

*The Reality of the other person
lies not in what he reveals to you
but in what he cannot reveal to you.
Therefore, if you would understand him,
listen not to what he says,
but rather to what he does not say.*

~ Kahlil Gibran — The Prophet ~

When the One Who Named You Has Forgotten Your Name

One of our greatest fears is the day when mom no longer knows us.

Or the evening when your wife is frightened by the strange man in her kitchen.

You.

As long as we are recognized by name, we feel that at some level, our connection is unbroken. But with each loss that dementia brings, a bit of our heart breaks. We fear it will break apart if we are no longer known.

If you are not there yet, know that for many, that day never comes.

If it does, the change is often gradual.

Your mother thinks that you are her sister one minute, and knows that you are her daughter the next. She understands that you are family, connected, and close, but which role you play in her life is muddled.

With dementia, the ability to name how we are connected may be lost. Immediate recognition of loved ones may fade. However, even those deep in dementia often recognize something, a deeper tie, to their loved ones than they do to other caregivers.

Their eyes light up, and they reach out.

They relax at your touch.

Some believe that it is no longer important to visit their loved one when they are not recognized, and when their time together is no longer remembered.

In all but very rare cases, I respectfully disagree.

A patient says that her daughter never visits, insists she hasn't heard from her in months. This, when her faithful daughter spends time with her three times a week and calls daily. Visiting when you are not remembered can be very painful, and some will choose not to go.

If you can spend time with your loved one, though, **please do**.

People with dementia live in the moment.

And so their joy is momentary. It is crucial to make a difference in the moments we can.

Living in the moment, not dwelling on the past or the future, these are the goals of meditation. "Be present in the now" is a mantra of mindfulness gurus. Indeed, no one can be said to be living more in the present than those who have lost their past and have no conception of the future.

If your loved one does reach this point, forgetting even you, find support for the grief of this terrible loss. It may be possible to let go of the need to be recognized.

This doesn't happen without pain, but it may mark a path to peace.

Truly when we are present in *the present* and share our presence with our loved ones, we connect on a deeper level. Some caregivers are uniquely able to share the gift of their presence. *It involves reading body language and connecting to emotions rather than thoughts and words.* It is a gift with which some people seem to be born.

It is also a skill that can be developed.

Alzheimer's disease and other related dementias are terminal illnesses.[40] Our bodies are comprised of interrelating parts, governed by the brain. As the brain is eroded by the plaques and tangles of Alzheimer's disease, the presence of Lewy bodies, or the damage of strokes, it ceases to keep other organs functioning. Death is the inevitable result of these terminal diseases unless another illness intervenes, and release arrives sooner.

You may be faced with the need to decide how much treatment you want your loved one to receive if a life-threatening illness or incident does occur.

As discussed in an earlier chapter, one of the documents included in medical charts involves end of life decisions. Whether it is called a Living Will, Health Care Directive, a POLST (Providers Orders for Life-Sustaining Treatment), or some other name, these documents give direction as to how to proceed when someone is in a terminal health crisis.

I have seen health care directives, signed by loving family members, ordering "full code" life support, including resuscitation and intubation (breathing tubes) for individuals who have severe dementia and other critical conditions.

I have seen Do Not Resuscitate and Do Not Intubate (DNR/DNI) orders for others in similar straits.

If you are lucky, you had time to talk to your loved one about these issues while they were able to express their wishes. Otherwise, it is another decision point that you and your family will have to negotiate.

Your loved one's health care provider may be able to assist. I encourage support from a social worker or a faith leader. You may wish to consult your lawyer as well.

Some individuals with dementia may be placed on hospice services through Medicare if the physician determines that their anticipated lifespan is short. Hospice services may be provided in your own house or apartment, in assisted living, a skilled nursing facility, or a hospice home. Social services, chaplain services, and nursing are a few of the components of the hospice program. Hospice services can be beneficial to both the patient and their family.[41]

Dementia is a disease that gradually takes away the mind of your loved one. You may feel that you have lost him or her already. It is long, long grief that you have been carrying down a rocky path. Yet, you will still be sad to say the final goodbye. They may have forgotten, but you have not.

Our spirit remains alive as long as we have breath. Allow yourself to grieve. May God bless your final parting.

Blessed are those who mourn,
for they will be comforted.

~ Matthew 5:4 ~

CHAPTER 12

BACK TO **THE BEGINNING**

Is Is

Dementia is a particularly difficult disease to live with, whether you have it or you are the caregiver.

We live in a society that does not accept any signs of aging well. Being told that you look young for your age is a high compliment. Acting young for your age is celebrated. The wisdom gained through years of learning and triumphing over challenges is largely dismissed.

Of course, we would all do well to maintain our physical health through exercise. Of course, we want to stay nimble intellectually. Yet as we grow older, our muscles, bones, nervous system, and organs show signs of wear. Our bodies develop disorders and diseases.

This is not our fault. It simply is.

Dementia is a disease of the brain. The brain, like any organ within our body, can malfunction, become diseased. Unlike other illnesses, however, a condition of the brain seems to bring forth shame, embarrassment, and fear.

When my mother developed lung cancer after smoking a couple of packs of cigarettes a day for seventy years, friends and family reacted with only love and acceptance. When someone receives a diagnosis of congestive heart failure, even when it is a result of years of inactivity and poor diet, the general reaction is one of support and caring.

Dementia comes out of nowhere, and there are no known foolproof strategies to avoid it.

Yet somehow, even though the brain is just one organ among many, diseases of the brain are received differently. As a society, if we are ever to make strides against diseases and conditions of the brain, we need to accept that, like any other part of us, it can fail.

Sometimes, the best advice is simply to allow the person to have their disease.

You cannot make it go away.

You cannot stop it.

You cannot bring your loved one back into your reality.

You may be able to make things easier. Walk together, sing together, laugh together, sit together, pray together.

Be together.

Heroes and Hope

Increasingly, I see stories of individuals receiving their diagnosis and choosing to publicly acknowledge it, committing to live each remaining day to the fullest. Some journal daily, documenting their journey honestly. They express fear and frustration, yet seek to find grace in each moment.

Others offer their assistance to others in the same position. Still, others participate in clinical trials in the hope that their involvement may bring about a future cure.

There is hope.

Research continues.

Neurologists believe that the brain may be more resilient than we thought. According to experts, the best way to delay the onset of dementia is to get plenty of exercise.[42] And learn new things.

Puzzles are good, but learning a new language or instrument is better.

Be creative, enjoy the outdoors, spend time building connections with family and friends.

Get a pet.

Listen to great music.

These are all things we can do to keep our brains as healthy and strong as possible. And then, if the dreaded diagnosis comes, practice self-love. Seek the support of people who accept you wholeheartedly, disease, and all. Reach out to your faith community and other community resources.

Meditate, pray, and remember: *wherever your mind may go, your spirit is whole.*

Lindy

> *I walked into the lobby of the assisted living community, glad to be back at work after a long and lovely two-week vacation.*
>
> *Just ahead of me, Lindy stood silently, looking at the floor. She glanced up. She saw me. She threw back her head and cried, "There you are! I've been waiting for you!"*
>
> *I walked forward into her open arms. We hugged long and hard, rocking side to side. "Let me look at you," Lindy said, as she cupped my face in her hands. She did not know where I had been or how long I had been gone.*
>
> *Lindy did not know my name or any of the myriad details of my life.*
>
> *She — knew me by heart.*
>
> *Just as I knew her.*

Lindy and I had a special relationship—we just got each other. We shared something beyond words, beyond thought, beyond memory. This is the way that we know our loved ones too. A meeting of the heart, rather than a meeting of the mind.

There is a world where the ordinary conventions of conversation and the details of day-to-day life do not exist. This is a world where dementia patients live. Their minds have wandered off, but their spirits remain whole. <u>They have much to teach us.</u>

As you walk this rock-strewn path, as a caregiver or one whose own mind is afflicted, my wish is that you will find those who can uphold you. We are only here together on this planet for a short time. I pray that each of you may spend that time held in love.

CHAPTER 13

ACKNOWLEDGMENTS

THIS WORK WOULD NOT have been possible without Presbyterian Homes & Services and its extraordinary DOVE team. Their focus on understanding dementia and providing exceptional, loving care continues to inspire me.

Many thanks also to the Alzheimer's Association, which works to provide support and services to people in the everyday struggle of caregiving, while also focusing forward on finding a cure.

To my colleagues at Leading Age and all the incredible leaders that I have come to know through membership in this stellar association—each one dedicated to improving the lives of elders—my gratitude.

This book would not have happened without the encouragement of my wonderful Women of Substance friends, who understand the trials brought on by dementia and the importance of a good story!

Thank you to Easter Lutheran Church for helping to sustain my faith.

Thanks to Evie Waack with sincere gratitude and affection.

Thanks to Dick Edwards, mentor, cheerleader and friend.

And thanks to Dana and Laura at Cresting Wave Publishing!

And finally, to my family—you have always granted me the grace to be my best self. You give me unconditional support and love. I know you by heart. You are my greatest gift.

Thank you.

CHAPTER 14

RECOMMENDED **READING**

- *The 36 Hour Day*, 6th Edition, Nancy L. Mace, MA. Peter V. Rabins, MD
- *Creating Moments of Joy Along the Alzheimer's Journey*, Jolene Brackey
- *Surviving Alzheimer's, 2nd Edition: Practical Tips and Soul-saving Wisdom for Caregivers*, Pamela Spenser Scott
- *Aging with Grace: What the Nun Study Teaches Us About Leading Longer, Healthier and More Meaningful Lives*, David Snowdon
- *Mayo Clinic on Alzheimer's Disease: Your Guide to Understanding, Treating, Coping and Caregiving*, written by the Alzheimer's Experts at Mayo Clinic
- *Still Alice*, Lisa Genova
- *Meet Me Where I Am: An Alzheimer's Care Guide*, Mary Ann Drummond
- *Dignity and Grace: Wisdom for Caregivers and Those Living with Dementia*, Janet L. Ramsey
- *Ambiguous Loss: Learning to Live with Unresolved Grief,* Pauline Boss
- *Forget Memory: Creating Better Lives for People with Dementia*, Anne Basting

CHAPTER 15

HELPFUL
WEBSITES

- Alzheimer's Disease and Related Dementias (ADEARS) *https://www.nia.nih.gov/alzheimers*
- Alzheimer's Association *https://www.alz.org*
- Alzheimer's Disease Center Mayo Clinic *https://mayo.edu*

CHAPTER 16

END NOTES

1   Dementia Symptoms and Causes. Mayo Clinic *https://mayoclinic.org* n.d.

2   Descartes 1637

3   Dementia Symptoms and Causes. Mayo Clinic *https://mayoclinic.org* n.d.

4   op.cit.

5   What Is Mixed Dementia? Alzheimer's Society August 17, 2018 *https://www. alzheimers.org.uk*

6   10 Early Signs and Symptoms of Alzheimer's; Alzheimer's Association *https://www.alz.org*

7   Aging and the Brain. Postgraduate Medical Journal R. Peters May 20, 2005 *https://www.ncbi.nim.nih.gov*

8   Brutal Truths About the Aging Brain. Discover Magazine Robert Epstein September 19, 2012 *https://discovermagazine.com*

9   Psychology of Emotions, Emotions and Memory. Psychologist World *https:// psychologistworld.com*

10 Amygdala-Hippocampus Dynamic Interaction in Relation to Memory. Richter-Levin, Akirav November 20, 2000

11 Stages of Dementia: The 3-Stage and the 7-Stage Models. Kindly Care, Molli Grossman *https://www.kindlycare.com*

12 Dementia Symptoms and Causes. Mayo Clinic n.d. *https://mayoclinic.org*

13 10 Signs of Frontotemporal Dementia. Alzheimer's Net Jennifer Wegerer May 15, 2014 *https://www.alzheimers.net*

14 op.cit

15 op.cit

16 What Is Lewy Body Dementia? National Institutes of Health *https://nia.nih.gov* n.d.

17 Lewy Body Dementia. Mayo Clinic *https://www.mayoclinic.org*

18 What Causes Visual Hallucinations in Dementia with Lewy Bodies? Christopher Morris Newcastle University November 2015 *https://www.alzheimers.org.uk*

19 Dementia with Lewy Bodies: An Emerging Disease. D. Neef et. al Am Fam Physician April 1, 2006

20 Early On-Set Alzheimer's. Mayo Clinic *https://www.mayoclinic.org* n.d.

21 Alzheimer's Disease Genetics Fact Sheet. National Institute on Aging *https://www.nia.nih.gov* n.d.

22 W. Edward Deming *https://blog.deming.org*

23 Depression in Dementia. National Institute of Health D. Kitching December 2015 *https://www.ncbi.nlm.nih.gov*

24 Sleep Issues and Sundowning. Alzheimer's Association *https://www.alz.org*

25 Eating and Common Behavior Challenges. Alzheimer's Society https://www.alzheimers.org.uk

26 How Alzheimer's Disease Affects Vision and Perception. Vision Aware, A. Demmitt n.d. *https://www.visionaware.org*

27 Language and Dementia Neurological Aspects. D. Kempler, M. Goral January 1, 2008 National Institutes of Health *https://www.ncbi.nlm.nih.gov*

28 Wandering and How to Address It. Mayo Clinic *https://www.mayoclinic.org* n.d.

29 op.cit

30 What is Anosognosia? Healthline.com T. Jewell, reviewed by T. Legg October 1, 2018 *https://www.healthline.com*

31 Using Reality Orientation in Alzheimer's and Dementia—Strategies and Cautions in its Use. Esther Heerema, MSW, medically reviewed by Claudia Chaves, MD November 24, 2019 Very Well Health *https://verywellhealth.com*

32 Building Cognitive Reserve *https://www.mempowered.com*

33 Understanding the Antecedent Behavior Consequence Model Better Help Dylan Buckley updated December 3, 2019

34 Language and Dementia Neurological Aspects. D. Kempler, M. Goral January 1, 2008 National Institutes of Health *https://www.ncbi.nlm.nih.gov*

35 The 5 Rs of Dementia Care. Word Press June 12, 2015 *https://thinkaboutthebrain.wordpress.com*

36 Minnesota Vulnerable Adults Act *https://www.ag.state.mn.us*

37 An Assessment of the Therapeutic Fib. D. Green February 21, 2014 *https://academicworks.cuny.edu*

38 Repetitive Behavior. Alzheimer's Society *https://www.alzheimers.org.uk* n.d.

39 Nursing Homes. AARP Public Policy Institute A.N. Houser October 2007 *https://www.aarp.org*

40 Dementia is a Terminal Illness Study. Medical News Today Catharine Paddock October 15, 2009

41 End of Life Care for People with Dementia. National Institute on Aging *https://www.nia.hih.gov*

42 Physical Exercise as a Preventative or Disease Modifying Treatment. PubMed JE Ahlskog, et.al. 2011 *https://www.ncbi.nim.nih.gov*